M000266622

AIRCRAFT WEAPONRY

OF TODAY

AIRCRAFT WEAPONRY
OF TODAY

ROY BRAYBROOK

Preceding pages:
The low-drag carriage of external stores is illustrated by the General Dynamics F-16XL, with bombs mounted in tandem on short pylons. (General Dynamics)

ISBN 0 85429 634 4

A **FOULIS** Aviation Book

First published 1988

© Haynes Publishing Group 1988

All rights reserved. No part of this book may be reproduced or transmitted in any form or by any means, electronic or mechanical, including photocopying, recording or by any information storage or retrieval system without permission of the publisher.

Published by:
Haynes Publishing Group
Sparkford, Nr. Yeovil, Somerset
BA22 7JJ. England.

Haynes Publications Inc.
861 Lawrence Drive, Newbury Park,
California 91320. USA.

British Library Cataloguing in Publication data
Braybrook, Roy
    Aircraft weaponry of today : an
    international survey.
    1. Air operations. Military equipment :
    Weapons
    I. Title
    335.8'2
ISBN 0-85429-634-4

Library of Congress catalog card number 88-81071

Editor: Mansur Darlington
Layout design: Mike King
Printed in England by: J.H. Haynes & Co.

Contents

Chapter I

Automatic Weapons

SINCE THE 1950s the emphasis in aircraft armament has been largely on guided weapons, rather than the traditional machine guns, cannon, rocket projectiles, and 'dumb' bombs. The guided weapon (GW), several types of which were pioneered by Germany during the Second World War, is a good means to deliver a large warhead precisely over a long range, giving a high kill probability with minimum risk to the launch aircraft. On the other hand such weapons are expensive, produce substantial drag when installed on the aircraft, and are generally useful against only one specific type of target. In the case of air-air engagements, GW are currently limited in minimum firing range (ie, it takes time for the guidance system to function effectively), and they place tight limits on combat persistence. A typical GW-armed fighter is restricted to perhaps four firings, although a fully-armed F-4 Phantom, F-14 Tomcat or F-15 Eagle carries eight missiles.

The older categories of aircraft armament are relatively inexpensive and operationally more flexible. In the case of automatic weapons (ie, machine guns and cannon) they clearly provide longer combat persistence than GW, and they have virtually no restriction on minimum firing range.

In the late 1960s and early 1970s the disadvantages of GW came to be appreciated, and there was fresh interest in exploiting the potential of simpler weapons, which had been virtually unchanged over a period of perhaps 20 years. Applying new concepts to warheads, fuses, and means of delivery, and funding R&D on a comparatively lavish scale, major advances were achieved across the spectrum of guns, bombs and rockets.

In effect, the armament manufacturers were filling in the cost-effectiveness gap between 'dumb' weapons and their highly sophisticated guided contemporaries. Carried to its logical conclusion, we will one day see aircraft cannon firing guided projectiles. In fact, work on the necessary technology is already in hand, although the concept seems likely to be used first in the heavier-calibre guns employed for air defences (ie, 35 mm upwards).

Machine guns and cannon (ie, automatic weapons firing explosive ammunition) represent some of the most flexible aircraft armaments, being used for both air-air and air-ground firings against a wide variety of targets. The first weapons carried in aircraft were handguns and rifles, but effective combat between aircraft would never have been possible without fast-firing guns that could exploit brief firing opportunities.

Fortunately, machine guns arrived before aircraft, as evidenced by the 37-barrel Belgian *Mitrailleuse* of 1851 and America's rotating-barrel

An early production Fairchild-Republic A-10A (serial 73-1665) firing the 30 mm GAU-8 cannon. Note the spread of the propellant gases, and the carriage of a 1-ton E-O guided bomb *(left)* and a 1-ton laser-guided bomb *(right)*. (Fairchild)

Gatling Gun of 1861. Neither was suitable for aircraft applications, but in 1884 the American-born Hiram Maxim (then a naturalized Briton residing in London) demonstrated a belt-fed, recoil-operated machine gun. This was adopted by many services, including those of Britain and Germany, where it was known as the Vickers and the 'Spandau' respectively.

There were various attempts to restrict the use of automatic weapons. The Declaration of St Petersburg in 1868 banned the use of explosive or incendiary projectiles weighing less than 0.88 lb (400 gm), and the Hague Conference of 1889 banned the discharging of *all* projectiles and explosives from any type of aerial machine. By 1907 this convention had been revoked, however, and the 1868 declaration (which would have ruled out cannon shells and incendiaries in all but the heaviest calibres) was quietly forgotten. Thus, by the time aeroplanes were flying dependably and were able to lift some form of warload, the legal restrictions were out of the way, and they could be armed without breaking the rules.

Britain, France, and Germany were all developing machine gun installations for aircraft by 1911, though the first automatic firing from an aeroplane in flight actually took place over Maryland on 2 June 1912. The aircraft was a two-seat Wright B biplane of the US Army Signal Corps, and the weapon was the rifle-calibre air-cooled, gas-operated, drum-fed Lewis. Lightweight variants of army machine guns represented the most significant category of aircraft armament in the First World War. Such guns continued in widespread use in the Second World War, with some countries (notably the US) employing the much heavier 0.50-inch (12.7 mm) calibre, but several European air forces had by this time introduced 20 mm cannon in order to defeat any foreseeable armour. The early leaders in this field were Hotchkiss, Hispano-Suiza and Oerlikon, although these companies were soon joined by Rheinmetall and Mauser. The Mauser MG213 revolver cannon was, in fact, just as significant historically as the original Gatling Gun.

Linear-Action Weapons

At the lower end of the scale, machine guns are still being produced that differ little from those used in the Second World War, although much more advanced ammunition is now available. Armour-piercing bullets of 12.7 mm calibre with cores of specially hardened steel can penetrate armour plate up to 20 mm thick, but this presumably refers to 90-degree impact at very short range. More realistically, the APHC-I projectile developed by Eurometall NV will penetrate 11.5 mm at 40 degrees at a range of 800 metres, a penetration equal to that of the 20 mm M95 AP-T round.

The 12.7 mm machine gun is almost three times as heavy as the 7.62 mm, but it throws a projectile that is over four times as heavy and will stop vehicles, whereas the rifle-calibre gun is basically an anti-personnel weapon. The 7.62 mm Browning of the Second World War weighed 22 lb

The FN (Fabrique Nationale Herstal SA) external mounting assembly (EMA) for the Bell and Agusta-Bell helicopter range, pictured here on a Bell 412. The assembly includes an AFSA II *(Affût Sabord)* (or door-mounted pintle head) for the 7.62 mm MAG 58 machine gun, an HMP (heavy machine gun pod, with 12.7 mm M3P and 230 rounds) and MRL 70 (modular rocket launcher with four 70 mm tubes). (FN)

(10 kg) and had a cyclic rate of 1100 rd/min. It threw a 10 gm projectile with a muzzle velocity of 2300–2600 ft/sec (700–800 m/sec). For comparison, a modern M3 of 12.7 mm weighs 64 lb (29 kg) and fires at 800–1200 rd/min. It throws a 45 gm bullet at 2800–3000 ft/sec (850–920 m/sec).

The basic concept of a single-barrel gun with a simple reciprocating action (recoil-operated, gas-operated, or a combination of the two) is similarly applied to cannon, though the rate of fire is limited by the time taken to extract a spent case and replace it with a new round. In the case of a helicopter weapon, a low rate of fire is generally acceptable, but for a fixed-wing aircraft a high rate of fire is required to achieve an air-air kill in (for example) a half-second burst.

Examples of linear-action cannon include the 20 mm Oerlikon KAD, GIAT M621 and M693, and Rheinmetall Rh202, the 25 mm Oerlikon KBA, and the 30 mm GIAT Type 781 and the McDonnell Douglas ASP-30. Looking at one of these cases in more detail, the **20 mm Oerlikon KAD** (formerly the HS.820) is a gas-operated cannon with provisions for a double-belt feed, allowing the gunner to select from two types of ammunition, eg. HEI

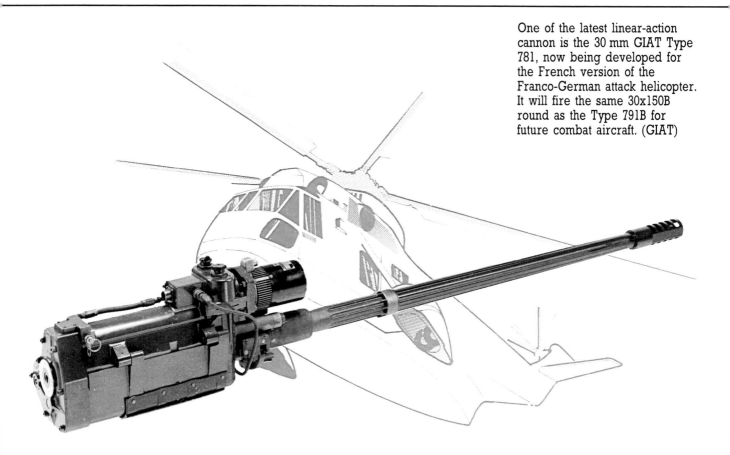

One of the latest linear-action cannon is the 30 mm GIAT Type 781, now being developed for the French version of the Franco-German attack helicopter. It will fire the same 30x150B round as the Type 791B for future combat aircraft. (GIAT)

for helicopters, and SAPHEI for armour. The KAD weighs 150 lb (68 kg), or 258 lb (117 kg) with its mounting cradle. It is capable of a cyclic rate of 1000 rd/min, but it is normally derated to 850 rd/min. The complete round weighs 0.675–0.798 lb (0.306–0.321 kg), and it throws a projectile weighing 0.275–0.320 lb (0.125–0.144 kg) at a muzzle velocity of 3400 ft/sec (1040 m/sec). Aside from a fixed mounting parallel to the longitudinal axis of the helicopter, the cannon may be pintle-mounted in the cabin doorway.

Heavier calibres generally provide longer ranges. The 7.62 mm machine gun may be effective in air-ground operation to around 500 metres, compared to 1000 metres for 12.7 mm. A 20 mm cannon extends

this range to the order of 1700 metres, and 25 mm increases this figure to perhaps 2200 metres. For comparison, helicopter-launched 80 mm unguided rocket projectiles may reach to 2500 metres, and anti-tank GW to 4000 metres. Armour penetration is illustrated by Oerlikon figures for SAPHEI rounds from the 20 mm KAD cannon and the 25 mm KBA, both impacting from a range of 800 metres and an angle of 60 degrees. The 20 mm penetrates 8 mm of armour and the 25 mm round goes through 18 mm. Even greater penetrations could be achieved with APDS

One example of a linear-action cannon is the 20 mm Oerlikon KAD, illustrated here on MBB's BO 105, with an ammunition-chute from the cabin left-hand side. (Oerlikon)

Dual-feed, enabling the operator to switch between two types of ammunition, is exemplified by this GIAT 25 mm Type 811. It was developed initially for the AMX-10 P25 mechanised infantry combat vehicle (MICV), which has the GIAT Dragar turret with 175 rounds of HE and 45 rounds of AP ammunition, but it is also suitable for air defence applications. (GIAT)

ammunition (34 mm in the case of the KBA), but the risk of the sabots entering the air intakes and damaging the engines places restrictions on the use of APDS. In any event, the instability and vibration of helicopters make them poor gun platforms for purposes other than area suppressive fire, hence it is doubtful whether the use of APDS rounds would be justified.

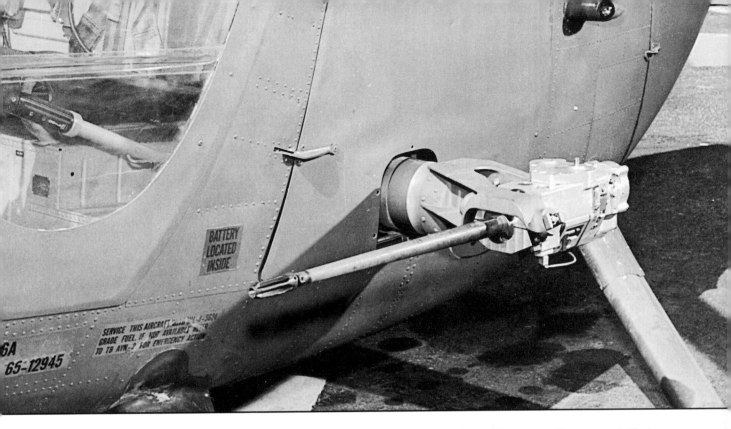

This discussion has so far been concerned only with self-powered weapons, which take the power required for loading and extraction from the energy produced by the burning of the propellant in the shell case. There are, however, disadvantages in such weapons, including the fact that a single misfire may stop the gun. In contrast, an externally-powered weapon will simply extract a round that has failed to fire, and continue to function regardless.

The **Chain Gun** is one example of an externally-powered weapon, developed by Hughes Helicopters (now the McDonnell Douglas Helicopter Co.) to combine the compact size of a self-powered weapon with the reliability of one that is externally powered. In essence, the reciprocating movement of the bolt is provided by the master-link in a chain that runs over four sprocket-wheels forming a rectangular 'racetrack'. Power is supplied to one of the sprockets, and the geometry of the chain-drive is arranged to hold the breech closed for as long as is necessary to minimise the escape of gases from the firing.

The smallest form of Chain Gun is the **7.62 mm EX-34,** which weighs 30 lb (13.6 kg), requires 0.3 hp, and fires at 570 rd/min. The next in the Chain Gun series is the **25 mm M242 Bushmaster**, which weighs 230 lb (104 kg), and has been produced in large numbers for ground vehicles. It fires, however, at only 100/200 rd/min, and has not so far been adapted to helicopter use. The most important of the series in an aviation context is the **30 mm M230** for the AH-64 Apache attack helicopter. The M230 weighs 123 lb (56 kg) and is derated from 900 to 625 rd/min. It is powered by a 6.5 hp motor and reaches its nominal speed in 0.2 sec. The complete system for the AH-64 weighs 1509 lb (684 kg) with 1200 rounds.

The externally-powered Chain Gun is a highly reliable and compact weapon. The smallest of the current range is the 7.62 mm EX-34 machine gun, shown here on a McDonnell Douglas Helicopter Co. OH-6A Cayuse, serial 65-12945. (McDonnell Douglas)

13

Revolver Cannon

Single-chamber linear-action guns are well suited to helicopter applications demanding only low rates of fire. They were used in fixed-wing aircraft during the Second World War, but the demand for increased cyclic rates led to alternative lines of development. Firing rate is limited by the component velocities and accelerations associated with loading and unloading each round. Even when the round has been made as short as possible, the gun is still restricted to around 1000 rd/min.

In seeking a solution to this problem, Mauser switched from a linear action to a revolver cannon, an enlarged and self-powered derivative of the cowboy's handgun. The new weapon had a rotating cylinder with five chambers, turned by the reciprocating action of a gas-operated slide. Whereas the cowboy's revolver used the cylinder as a convenient form of magazine, Mauser's **MG213C** revolver cannon used it to break down the operating cycle into a series of stages, making the feeding of the new round into the chamber a two-part action. This allowed the time between shots to be reduced to only a fraction of the complete cycle time, hence a far higher rate of fire could be achieved. The linear-action, single-chamber MG213A had been limited to 1100 rd/min, but the 20 mm MG213C/20 revolver cannon achieved a remarkable 1500 rd/min, a genuine breakthrough. The 30 mm Mauser MG213C/30 began its trials at a similar rate, but had to be slowed to 1200 rd/min due to barrel wear.

The wartime MG213C series spawned a variety of postwar derivatives, including America's 20 mm M39 (still used on the F-5E), and the 30 mm British Aden and corresponding French **DEFA 553** (both used in the Jaguar). The M39 is approaching the end of its life, but the Aden and DEFA soldier on in improved forms. The 25 mm **Aden-25** combines the well-proven revolver principle with a new generation of ammunition (STANAG 4173), exemplified by the Oerlikon KBA round, and a far higher cyclic rate, which is increased from 1200–1400 rd/min to 1650–1850 rd/min. Muzzle velocity is increased from the 2600 ft/sec (790 m/sec) of the Aden-30 to 3450 ft/sec (1050 m/sec). The Aden-25 is planned for the Harrier GR5 and the Hawk 200. Interestingly, although there was a general switch to electrical ignition for cannon shells at the end of the war, there is now a tendency to revert to percussion ignition in order to avoid the risk of inadvertent firing due to radar emissions while the aircraft is on the ground.

The **DEFA 554** is a less radical redesign, retaining the ammunition used in the Model 553, though the firing rate is increased from 1300 to 1800 rd/min. As far as can be judged from published information, this improvement has been achieved largely by breaking the loading action into three stages rather than two, by making use of a chamber that was previously idle for part of the cycle. The stroke of the ram is thus reduced from one half to a third of the length of the round, making possible an increase in cyclic rate of almost 50 per cent. The DEFA 554 is fitted to the Mirage 2000 and the Brazilian AMX, with pilot selection of cyclic rate of 1100 rd/min for air-ground use and 1800 rd/min for air-air firings.

France's DEFA 553 was fitted to all early Mirage variants and the Sepecat Jaguar. This 30 mm revolver cannon is shown here in the form of a two-gun pack with shell boxes mounted between the weapons. The photograph was taken at Le Bourget in 1973, in front of a Mirage 5 that had evidently been used for laser ranging trials and tests with Dassault's patented *'moustaches'* (retractable canards). (Roy Braybrook)

The latest British development in the revolver cannon category is the Aden-25, which combines a rate of fire of up to 1850 rd/min with the use of the very powerful 25x137 ammunition employed by the Oerlikon KBA, GIAT 811, and America's GAU-12/U, M242 Bushmaster, and GE 225. (Royal Ordnance)

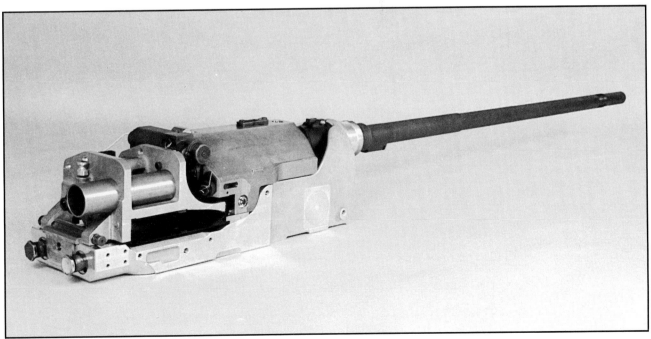

It may be that France adopted a less radical approach for the DEFA 554 because a completely new gun (the **Type 791B**) was planned for the Rafale D/ACE for the mid-1990s. Very little has been published on the 791B, beyond the fact that it weighs 242 lb (110 kg) and has a nominal rate of 2500 rd/min, with provisions for the pilot to select 1500 rd/min or even 300-600 rd/min. The maximum rate of fire is extremely high for a single-barrel gun, and it seems likely that this is associated with pilot-selection of a burst of very short duration, eg, 0.5 sec.

Prior to the Aden-25 and DEFA 554, the fastest-firing revolver cannon was probably the **27 mm Mauser BK27** used in the Tornado and the German version of the Alpha Jet. Although details have not been released, it is generally believed that the BK27 is fired at 1000 rd/min air-ground and 1700 rd/min air-air. Of revolver cannons already in service, the other outstanding example is the **30 mm Oerlikon KCA** used in the Viggen JA37. The cyclic rate is a relatively conservative 1350 rd/min, but the KCA uses a massive 1.96 lb (0.89 kg) shell, which throws a 0.79 lb (0.36 kg) projectile at 3380 ft/sec (1030 m/sec). The KCA is, however, a very large gun weighing 300 lb (136 kg), and is thus limited in potential applications.

France's response to the Aden-25 is the GIAT Type 791B, which is expected to give the next fighter generation a firing rate up to 2500 rd/min, and employs the 30x150B round. (GIAT)

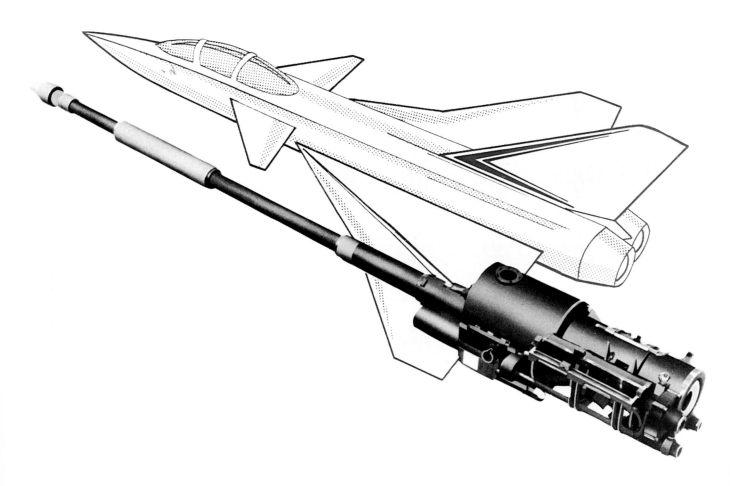

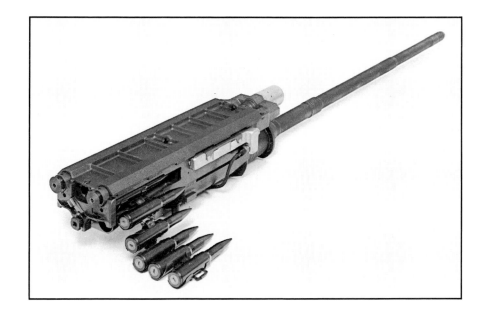

The most powerful revolver cannon currently in service is probably the 30 mm Oerlikon KCA fitted to the Saab JA37 fighter. It fires the massive 30x173 round, but it is such a large gun that it is difficult to instal. (Oerlikon)

Two Barrels

By divorcing the time between shots from the time taken to extract one case and insert the next live round, the revolver cannon made possible a much higher rate of fire from a single-barrel gun. Further improvement then suggested the use of two barrels, making possible firing rates of around 3500 rd/min. Some gun designers also appear to have been attracted to the two-barrel concept simply because they liked the idea of using the recoil on one side to activate the loading on the other.

The first two-barrel gun of significance was Germany's **Gast Gun** of the First World War. Developed as a replacement for the Parabellum LMG 14 (a lightweight derivative of the Maxim for flexible mounting), the Gast Gun fired the same 7.92 mm round, but at up to 1800 rd/min instead of the 700 rd/min of the LMG 14. It was fed by two 192-round drum magazines, one of which was placed vertically on each side of the weapon. Designed by Ingenieur Carl Gast, it was tested in the spring of 1918, but never saw active service. Postwar tests by the Allied nations showed impressive performance and reliability, but the idea was not further developed.

The two-barrel gun next appeared in the West in the mid-1950s, when Hughes Helicopters began development of the **20 mm Mk 11** cannon. Operated by a combination of gas pressure and recoil forces, the Mk 11 had an eight-chamber cylinder and two belt-feeds. It simultaneously rammed two cartridges, fired two, and ejected two empty cases. Firing rate was 4200 rd/min. The basic gun weighed 240 lb (109 kg), but it was most frequently used by the USN, USMC and Israeli Air Force as the **Mk 4 gunpod,** weighing 1390 lb (630 kg) with 750 rounds. Some 1000 pods were produced and delivered in the period 1965-67.

The Soviet Union developed its own twin-barrel cannon in the form of the **GSh-23,** which is usually mounted on the lower surface of the parent aircraft, and fed from a magazine within the fuselage. The GSh-23 first appeared on the MiG-21 in the form of the **GP-9** ventral pod (containing 200 rounds) during the mid-1960s. The Soviets then reconsidered the installation and produced a much neater scheme with 220 rounds in the fuselage. Similar designs were produced for other aircraft, including the MiG-23 and the Czech L-39 trainer. The IAR-93 developed jointly by Yugoslavia and Romania has two internal GSh-23Ys and a firing rate of 3500 rd/min per gun is claimed. The GSh-23 is reported to weigh only 160 lb (72 kg) and to fire a 200 gm projectile at a muzzle velocity of 2900 ft/sec (890 m/sec).

The Soviet Union's twin-barrel GSh-23 is illustrated here as installed below the front fuselage of the Czech L-39 trainer. The aerodynamic fairing is lowered for ease of access, but the welded-steel blast deflector (to minimise pitch-down due to gunfire) is evidently fixed permanently to the fuselage. (Aero Vodochody)

Before leaving the subject of two-barrel cannon, it may be noted that the new gun for the USAF Advanced Tactical Fighter (ATF) will probably have either two or three barrels. During the late 1970s the service funded two 30 mm technology demonstrators under the **Compact High-performance Aerial Gun (CHAG)** programme. The Ford contender was a 260 lb (110 kg) gun with two fixed barrels, while General Electric proposed a three-barrel modified Gatling that weighed 280 lb (127 kg). These demonstrators were intended to establish a base from which future guns could be developed, and it seems reasonable to suppose that the ATF cannon will follow one configuration or the other.

More recently, GE has become interested in the two-barrel gun concept, resurrecting the Gast principle as the basis for the **25 mm Lightweight Gun.** In essence, two gas-operated guns are mounted side-by-side, with the pressure created in the barrel being tapped to a cylinder in which a piston is forced aft, providing the impetus for extraction and ejection of the spent case. In this instance, the reciprocating action of the two bolts is linked by means of an interconnecting lever, so that extraction on one side is co-ordinated with forward bolt movement and firing on the other. The company has also tested the gun with the gas system disconnected and the interconnecting lever oscillated by means of an electric drive. The GE 25 mm Lightweight Gun or GE 225 weighs 190 lb (86 kg), compared to the 230 lb (104 kg) of the 25 mm M242 Chain Gun. When gas operated, it fires at up to 2000 rd/min, and when externally-powered it has fired at up to 750 rd/min.

Multi-Barrel Guns

The revolver concept pioneered by Mauser in the closing phases of the Second World War offered the prospect of firing rates approaching 2000 rd/min, but the USAF decided in 1946 to fund a much more ambitious development, aimed at combining far higher rates of fire with outstanding reliability. The result was Project Vulcan, in which General Electric was to revive the 1861 Gatling concept, using electrical power in place of the original hand crank.

The Gatling Gun consists of a cluster of parallel barrels that rotate about a common axis, each barrel having its own bolt to feed, fire, and extract the rounds of ammunition. The bolt is moved backwards and forwards by a follower that rides in a cam-track on the fixed housing of the gun.

The outcome of this project was the 20 mm, six-barrel **M61A1 Vulcan** gun, which became the standard USAF weapon for the F-104 Starfighter and F-105 Thunderchief from 1958, and has equipped most USAF and USN fighters since that date. The M61 fires at 6000 rd/min as standard, and up to 7200 rd/min if required. It weighs 252 lb (114 kg), and has a muzzle velocity of 3380 ft/sec (1030 m/sec). Considering as a typical installation that of the F-16, the feed system weighs 293 lb (133 kg) and 512 rounds weigh 287 lb (130 kg), giving a system weight of 831 lb (377 kg). The F/A-18 installation weighs 841 lb (381 kg) with 570 rounds.

By the time these words are published the selection of a cannon for the Eurofighter EFA will presumably have been made, and (regardless of the final choice) it is of interest that GE proposed an **Improved M61** for this application. The weight of the gun is reduced from 252 lb (114 kg) to 205 lb (93 kg), due to lightweight material improvements and component weight reductions. Because of the reduced weight, the Improved M61 accelerates to its design firing rate (4000 rd/min) in a shorter time, viz, 0.25 sec. With a 291-round linear linkless feed system (LLFS), the projected system would weigh 467 lb (212 kg).

As an alternative to saving weight, GE proposed an increase in barrel length from 56 to 75 inches (142 to 190 cm), to produce a higher muzzle velocity. The company also suggested the use of the GE 'Aim-Guns'

HUD-WAC system, the new PGU-28/B SAPHEI ammunition, and Raufoss-type fuse. This fuse is estimated to give a 20 per cent increase in the probability of a kill, given a hit. Aside from the attractions of commonality with existing fighters, the M61 is claimed to exhibit an MRBF (mean rounds between failures) of more than 100,000 or 20,000 plus for the overall system, compared to 200–1500 rounds for single-barrel guns.

One of the advantages of the Gatling principle is that a family of guns can be developed in any chosen calibre, varying the number of barrels to suit the rate of fire required. For example, after the six-barrel M61, GE produced the three-barrel **M197,** with a firing rate of 750 or 1500 rd/min. The M197 has been used in both the M97 helicopter turret (also on the OV-10) and in pintle-mounted form, the latter being further derated to 700 or even 350 rd/min. It is also employed in the **GPU-2/A pod,** firing at 750 or 1500 rd/min, and weighing 586 lb (266 kg) with 300 rounds.

The second major Gatling to emerge from GE was the 30 mm seven barrel **GAU-8/A Avenger** for the Fairchild A-10 anti-tank aircraft. Despite the number of barrels, the GAU-8/A fires at a comparatively modest 2100/4200 rd/min, the A-10 pilot selecting the rate according to tactical

The largest of GE's Gatling series is the seven-barrel 30 mm GAU-8/A, which occupies a considerable percentage of the front fuselage volume of the A-10, as shown by this photograph taken at Farnborough in 1976. (Roy Braybrook)

demands. The basic gun weighs 620 lb (281 kg), but the full installation of the A-10 amounts to 4030 lb (1828 kg) with 1350 rounds. This gun also introduced a new family of ammunition with aluminium cases for reduced weight, and an API round with a depleted uranium (DU) core. This round

The relatively modest maximum level speed of the A-10, viz 368 knots (682 km/hr), permits a high-drag gun installation, with plenty of ventilating air. (Fairchild)

The A-10 was designed around the General Electric GAU-8/A in order to ensure a high probability of killing a tank in a single strafing pass. (Fairchild)

weighs 748 gm, and throws a 430 gm projectile with a muzzle velocity of 3000 ft/sec (980 m/sec), allowing it to arrive at a distance of 1200 metres with 14 times the kinetic energy of the standard US 20 mm API round. The HEI round of the GAU-8/A likewise delivers six times the energy of the earlier 20 mm round.

One derivative of the GAU-8/A is the four-barrel **GAU-13/A,** which fires the same ammunition at a rate of 2400 rd/min. The basic gun weighs 339 lb (151 kg), but its most common application is the GPU-5/A pod, which weighs 1900 lb (862 kg) with 350 rounds. This pod is also referred to as the GEPOD-30 or Pave Claw, and it is widely used on USAF F-4Es and A-7Ds, and on some export F-5Es.

The Northrop F-20 Tigershark test-firing a General Electric GPU-5/A pod, housing the GAU-13/A four-barrel derivative of the 30 mm seven-barrel gun carried by the A-10. Note the downward deflection of propellant gases, to counteract the nose-down pitch caused by the recoil of the gun. (Northrop)

The other GE Gatling Gun in the 30 mm class is the three barrel **XM-188E1,** which was developed to fire Aden/DEFA ammunition, and is thus a far smaller, lighter gun than the GAU-8/A. Its overall length of 56.75 inches (144 cm) compares with 114 inches (289.6 cm) for the GAU-8/A, and its weight of 111 lb (50 kg) is less than 20 per cent of that for the large gun.

The latest cannon in the Gatling series is the five-barrel 25 mm **GAU-12/U Equalizer,** which was developed for the AV-8B. The gun weighs 270 lb (122 kg) and fires at 3600 rd/min, producing a muzzle velocity of 3600 ft/min (1097 m/sec). The AV-8B installation consists of two

One of the most recent of GE's Gatling developments is the five-barrel 25 mm GAU-12/U Equalizer for the McDonnell Douglas AV-8B Harrier II, firing the Bushmaster round at a cyclic rate of 3600 rd/min. (General Electric)

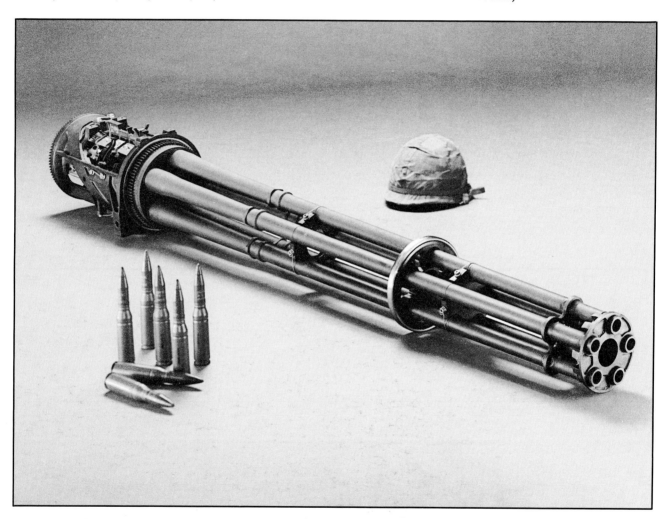

ventral pods, the left one housing the gun and the right one 300 rounds of ammunition, the two being connected by a faired ammunition chute. The GAU-12/U was designed around the highly lethal Bushmaster family of ammunition, but GE is developing a new API round, presumably to replace the standard APDS.

This discussion of GE's Gatling Guns would not be complete without mention of the two machine guns in the series. One of the most widely used of postwar guns is the **7.62 mm GAU-2B/A Minigun,** which has six barrels and fires at 6000 rd/min with a muzzle velocity of 2750 ft/sec (838 m/sec). It is used internally on the AT-37, in the form of the **SUU-11B/A pod** for the AT-38, in a turret for the AH-1G, UH-1N, and OH-58, and with a pintle mounting for the UH-1H/N, HH-53, and SH-3A helicopters, in addition to the MXU-470 module for the AC-119 gunship.

The six-barrel GAU-2B/A 7.62 mm Minigun has appeared in many forms on both fixed- and rotary-wing aircraft. It was photographed here on an Aermacchi MB-339 prototype (serial MM.389) at Le Bourget in 1977. (Roy Braybrook)

A recent derivative of this concept is the **GECAL-50,** a 12.7 mm Gatling developed primarily for helicopters. It is available with either three or six barrels, weighing 66 lb (30 kg) or 96 lb (43.5 kg) respectively. Maximum rate of fire is 8000 rd/min. The GECAL-50 is proposed in the form of a three-barrel composite-construction turret for the USMC V-22 Osprey, with a 1150 round linkless feed system giving a rate of fire up to 2000 rd/min and a system weight of 313 lb (142 kg). Pintle-mounted installations are proposed for various helicopters, with linked ammunition giving a rate of fire up to 4000 rd/min. With increased interest in the air-air combat scenario, GE emphasises that standard NATO 12.7 mm M-8 API rounds easily penetrate 0.25-inch (0.64 cm) armour at 1500 metres range. Press reports indicate that an important factor in the promotion of the GECAL-50 was operational experience provided by the Grenada invasion, in which helicopter-mounted 7.72 mm suppression weapons proved largely ineffective.

Guns of the Future

There is still considerable scope for improving aerial cannon, especially for the air-air role. The general demands remain much the same as they were when cannon were first introduced: to throw a great deal of explosive in a short burst; to achieve a high probability of a hit; and to achieve a high probability of a kill in the event of a hit. In addition, designers still strive to reduce the cost and weight of ammunition, primarily by using less expensive and lighter materials for shell cases.

The USAF planned a new gun to match the development of the F-15, and Philco-Ford was contracted for the **25 mm GAU-7/A.** This was to have been a radical new gun using caseless ammunition (thus eliminating the time taken conventionally for case extraction), but it ran into problems with ammunition storage and uneven propellant burning, hence the F-15 retained the well-established M61.

Caseless ammunition may still be some way in the future, and the same probably applies to the use of liquid propellants. On a more modest scale, there are reports of plastic cases, which could be significantly cheaper than metal. Ford Aerospace is developing 'cased telescoped' ammunition in which the projectile is surrounded by propellant within a cylindrical steel case. This arrangement produces a much shorter round, making possible higher cyclic rates. Some reports suggest that it also provides far higher muzzle velocities, in the region of 5000 ft/sec (1500 m/sec).

Telescoped ammunition is to be an important feature of the new gun for the USAF's ATF. The gun is expected to be an inverse Gatling (ie, the barrels will not rotate) with two or three barrels giving a cyclic rate in the region of 5000 rd/min.

Another advanced feature that has been under active development for some time is the ability to adjust the path of projectiles leaving the gun in order to correct for small aiming errors in the parent aircraft. Such corrections might be obtained by allowing some flexibility in the gun mounts, or by actually bending the barrels of the gun. Ford Aerospace is known to have done some work in this field, using hydraulic actuators to bend a gun barrel through two or three degrees from its normal axis.

For the longer term there appears a good chance that some aircraft cannon shells will be guided, although the system of guidance may be primitive in comparison with that of a full-scale air-air GW, and it may require somewhat larger calibres than are currently used for aircraft cannon. Several companies are already working on course-corrected, spin-stabilised shells to counter manoeuvring targets. For example, British Aerospace is working in collaboration with OTO Melara on a system in which command guidance signals are transmitted to 76 mm shells. Raytheon has meanwhile demonstrated the ability to correct the course of a 40 mm projectile in flight, using impulses produced by small explosive charges. It is anticipated that the system of course correction may be applied to shells as small as 20 mm, and that various guidance concepts (including strapdown seekers and command links) may be used.

Course-correctable 40 mm projectiles, controlled by jets produced by small explosive charges. (Raytheon)

Chapter 2

Unguided Rockets

IN THE FIELD of low-cost weapons, automatic cannon (as described in the preceding chapter) provide an attractive combination of destructive power and operational flexibility, but they are limited in range (since their projectiles are decelerating from the moment they leave the barrel) and in the size of warhead that they can deliver. During the Second World War cannon of up to 75 mm calibre were used in aircraft, but only in relatively small-scale specialised operations.

For tank-busting the Ju 87G-1 was given a pair of 37 mm BK3,7 Flak 18 cannon, and the Hurricane IIDs (and some Mk IVs) were given two 40 mm cannon. The Luftwaffe made limited use of the 75 mm BK7,5 PaK 40 cannon on the Ju 88P-1 and the He 129-3. For anti-ship strikes, the Mosquito FB XVIII was equipped with the 57 mm six-pounder Molins Gun, and the B-25H carried the incredible armament of 14x12.7 mm machine guns and a 75 mm gun that fired 15 lb (6.8 kg) projectiles. Only 27 Mosquito XVIIIs were built, but North America completed no less than 1000 B-25Hs for use in the Pacific. A 108 mm gun was tested in Italy's four-engined Piaggio P-108 bomber, but it was too late to see service. In Vietnam the Pave Aegis AC-130H's armament included a 105 mm howitzer.

The fact that what was almost certainly the heaviest gun ever used operationally in the Second World War by a production aircraft fired only a 15 lb (6.8 kg) projectile in a single-shot (manually reloaded) mode is a good indication of the limitations of barrel-fired weapons in the air-surface role. In the air-air role, achieving a high probability of a target kill with a short burst of automatic fire generally requires a range not significantly greater than 500 metres. To put these figures in perspective, the first

28

Second World War generation of unguided rockets provided an air-air range of the order of 1000 metres (ie, twice that of cannon), and the standard British 3-inch (76 mm) rocket made it possible for a single-engined fighter to deliver eight 60 lb (27 kg) warheads in an air-surface attack. It was with this latter armament that the Hawker Typhoon proved its value in supporting the Normandy landings of 1944, some 137 German tanks being destroyed in one attack alone.

The air-air use of rockets was tested as early as 1916-17, when some Allied fighting scouts had Le Prieur rockets on tubular launch-rails mounted at a large inclination on the interplane struts. The BE.2e carried four, the DH.2 six, the Nieuport 16, 17 and 23 up to eight, and the BE.12 up to 10. The objective was to destroy hydrogen-filled ballons and airships, the most noteworthy success being the destruction of Zeppelin L.48 on 17 June 1917 by BE.12 No 6610 of No 37 Sqn RFC, flown by Lt L.P. Watkins.

The Le Prieur rocket was effectively superseded by improved rifle-calibre incendiary ammunition. For practical purposes air-air rockets were then forgotten until the Second World War, when Germany produced much more lethal designs as a desperate measure to improve the Luftwaffe's success rate against heavy Allied bombers.

In destroying a large aircraft there is (short of nuclear weapons) no real substitute for sheer weight of explosive, which means a long burst of well-aimed cannon fire, or a single strike or near miss by a rocket projectile. The principal German weapon of the Second World War in this

A Hawker Hunter FGA9 of No 54 Sqn, XF523/N, firing the old 3-inch RPs with 60 lb (27 kg) warheads, which were extremely inaccurate, but useful for knocking down mud forts. (Crown Copyright)

29

Armament options for the AV-8B. From front to rear: four AIM-9Ls, four 577 lb
(262 kg) LAU-10 and six 216 lb (98 kg) LAU-68 rocket pods, six 542 lb (246 kg)
LAU-61s and four LAU-68s, six LAU-10s and four LAU-61s, ten Mk 77 520 lb
(236 kg) firebombs, ten Mk 20 490 lb (222 kg) bombs, sixteen Mk 82 530 lb
(240 kg) LDGP bombs and a TER, six Mk 83 LDGP 985 lb (447 kg) bombs and
four TERs. (McDonnell Douglas)

category was the 55 mm R4M folding-fin unguided rocket. Several variants of the Me 262 could carry 24 of these missiles (48 on the experimental Me 262E), attached to two fairings under the outer wings.

Weapon delivery from outside the defensive fire of USAAF bombers was nonetheless uncertain, so various heavy and more accurate projectiles were tested. One system for the Me 262D involved the upward firing of a dozen 50 mm SG-500 *Jagdfaust* (Fighter's Fist) mortar bombs, triggered by a photo-electric cell as the fighter passed below the bomber.

In the early postwar period, Britain's RAF initially concentrated on developing the 30 mm Aden revolver cannon to replace the 20 mm Hispano, then in the 1950s made desperate efforts to develop air-air guided weapons, although the Lightning that entered service in 1960 also had provisions for 48x2-inch (51 mm) rockets (originally developed for RN use) in two packs in the lower front fuselage. For air-ground use the Second World War 3-inch (76 mm) rocket was retained on Hunters into the 1960s, when it was finally replaced by the French **SNEB 68 mm,** carried in pods developed by Matra.

The SA.365M, the military version of the Dauphin 2, armed a Thomson-Brandt Type 68-22 launcher for 68 mm SNEB rockets, and a GIAT 20 mm M621 gunpod. (Aérospatiale)

The conical-nose Type 155 practice launcher carries 18 rounds, and the original rounded-nose operational Type 116M carried 19, the extra rocket being housed on the pod centreline to break the plastic nose-cap and thus clear the way for the remaining rounds.

It now appears, however, that the frangible-nose concept has been abandoned (presumably due to the risk of damage to the adjacent structure). Matra consequently produces an operational Type 155 with individual covers over the 18 tubes. The company also produces the operational 36-round Type F1, the six-round F2, which is used both for training and to arm light aircraft and, the reduced-weight 18-round Type H56 for helicopters. Matra launchers may be used on a single shot basis, or (depending on type) to fire salvoes of 3,6 18 or 36 rounds at a rate of 1800-2000 rd/min. Thomson-Brandt makes 12- and 18-round 68 mm unfaired launchers for helicopters.

It may be noted that in the Falklands conflict the RAF Harriers were cleared to fire the naval 2-inch (51 mm) rocket in place of the 68 mm SNEB in order to simplify logistics while operating from RN carriers, and to avoid any possible problems associated with radar hazards (ie, the possibility of an inadvertent firing due to the carrier's emissions).

The SNEB 68 mm rocket is very light (weighing from 4.29 to 6.2 kg depending on the type of warhead), and is stated to be capable of piercing

A British Aerospace Buccaneer S2B, serial XT270, firing two 18-round Matra Type 155 launchers of 68 mm SNEB rockets. (Royal Air Force)

The large inverted store in front of this French Air Force Alpha Jet from the CEAM test centre at Mont-de-Marsan (BA-118) is the Dassault-Breguet CEM-1, the training version of which combines 18 rockets with four practice bombs. The operational version combines rockets with bombs or a grenade launcher, and the reconnaissance version has four cameras in the nose. (Roy Braybrook)

armour up to 400 mm thick. For any shaped-charge warhead, the depth of armour penetration is roughly proportional to its diameter, hence rockets of larger calibre may be required for specially hard targets. In addition to the SNEB 68 mm, Thomson-Brandt therefore also produces a **100 mm rocket,** which is generally carried in a four-round pod, although a six-round unit is also available. The hollow-charge warhead of the 100 mm can penetrate 600 mm of steel.

The RAF has not adopted a heavy rocket, preferring to rely on the use of cluster bombs to destroy armour. In selecting an anti-armour weapon for the Hunter (the only recent British combat aircraft to be exported in

The rocket launcher in the foreground is a Thomson-Brandt Type 100-4, which weighs 529 lb (240 kg) with four 100 mm rockets with DEM warheads. The weapons carrier on the Mirage F1 in the background provides a low-drag mounting for four Matra Durandal runway-piercing bombs. (Roy Braybrook)

worthwhile numbers), Hawker Aircraft chose the Hispano 81 mm rocket, which is now known as the **Oerlikon SURA,** and which equips most overseas aircraft of this series. The SURA is unusual in that its cruciform tailfins are slotted and slide forwards along the body of the rocket to form a mounting point, lower rounds in a tier engaging with the tailfins of the round above. Oerlikon also produces the **81 mm SNORA,** which was developed in collaboration with Italy's SNIA-Viscosa, and is fired from conventional 12-round pods.

Lynx helicopter firing 80 mm Oerlikon SURA rockets. (Westland)

The Oerlikon 80 mm SURA rocket, illustrating how these weapons are stacked by means of interlocking tail-fins. On firing, each rocket in turn slides through its own tail assembly, then jerks it out of engagement with the supporting round. (Oerlikon)

35

To revert to the story of early postwar rocket developments, the US produced two families of projectiles, the **2.75-inch (70 mm) FFAR** (Folding Fin Aircraft Rocket) or 'Mighty Mouse' and the **5-inch (127 mm) HVAR** (High Velocity Aircraft Rocket) or Zuni, both of which remain in the inventory today. The FFAR was a particularly important weapon, being adopted in many Western countries and serving as the basis for several later developments. It was initially used (like the preceding German R4M) to produce a shotgun effect against large bombers, being fitted to early USAF jet fighters such as the North American F-86D, Lockheed F-94C and Northrop F-89D. When air-air guided missiles such as the AIM-9 Sidewinder (also developed by the US Navy) became available, the FFAR was relegated to the surface attack role.

Being designed for high-speed launch, the FFAR was the subject of some criticism when it was used from helicopters in Vietnam, especially when firings took place at the hover. In order to improve accuracy by reducing the time that the rocket spends in the downwash of the rotor, the US Army and Navy jointly developed the **Hydra-70** series, which retains the 70 mm calibre of the FFAR, but uses the faster burning (and less visible) Mk 66 motor in place of the Mk 40. The Hydra-70 is manufactured by BEI Defense Systems, and two types of lightweight launcher are being built by Hughes Aircraft, the 7-tube M260 and the 19-tube M261, for use on the US Army AH-1 attack helicopter.

Another important rocket development of the same calibre is the **CRV7 (Canadian Rocket Vehicle 7),** which was developed under the direction of the Department of National Defence in Ottawa, and is produced by Bristol Aerospace at Winnipeg. The CRV7 is available with two motors, the C14 for fixed-wing use and the faster-burning C15 for helicopters. Relative to the old FFAR, the CRV7 makes possible improved accuracy, firing ranges increased to around 8000 metres, and the use of shallow dive angles. The high velocity of the projectile also facilitates the use of kinetic energy penetrator warheads, with rods of hardened steel or tungsten in a plastic shell. Operationally the CRV7 is fired from a disposable 19-tube launcher (LAU-5003 A/A), or, in the case of a helicopter, the reusable 6-tube LAU-5002 A/A.

Belgium's **Les Forges de Zeebrugge (FZ)** began making the FFAR under licence from the US Navy in 1956, manufacturing both the Mk 4 Mod 10 for high performance aircraft and the Mk 40 Mod 3 for helicopters and slow fixed-wing aircraft. The company then developed a second generation, based on motors of over 90 per cent greater total impulse, known as the FZ67 for fixed-wing use and the FZ68 for helicopters. A third generation has the designation NR.96. The same manufacturer makes 7-tube LAU-51 and 19-tube LAU-32 pods for high performance aircraft, and the 7-tube M.157C, the unfaired 12-tube LAU-103, and the 19-tube M.159C for slower aircraft.

Space restrictions permit only a mention of some of the other unguided rockets produced by various countries. **Brazil's Avibras** manufactures the 37 mm SBAT-37, which is fired from a 7-round launcher

Test-firings of the BEI Defense Systems Hydra-70 rocket from the Hughes Aircraft 19-round M261 pod, mounted on the outboard pylons of this AH-64 Apache. (McDonnell Douglas)

The Avibras LM-70/7 launcher, housing seven 70 mm SBAT-70 rockets, and mounted on a Brazilian Navy Wasp helicopter. (Avibras)

(LM-37/7), and the SBAT-70 and -127, which are reportedly similar to the FFAR and HVAR respectively, the latter delivering a 44 lb (20 kg) warhead. China employs the 90 mm Type 1 rocket, fired from a Type HF-7 launcher and produced by NORINCO (China North Industries Corp). Italy's **Aerea** manufactures a range of pods for the SNORA, FFAR, and a 50 mm rocket by SNIA-BPD.

The Soviet Union's most commonly used rocket is the 57 mm S-5, fired from the 16-round UV-16-57 pod, but there is also the 137 mm M-100, the 160 mm S-16, the 190 mm TRS-190, the 212 mm ARS-212, the 220 mm S-21,

This Czech Air Force L-39 Albatross trainer is equipped with a Soviet UV-16-57 pod outboard (with 16 57 mm rockets) and a 77 imp gal (350 litre) tank inboard. (Aero Vodochody)

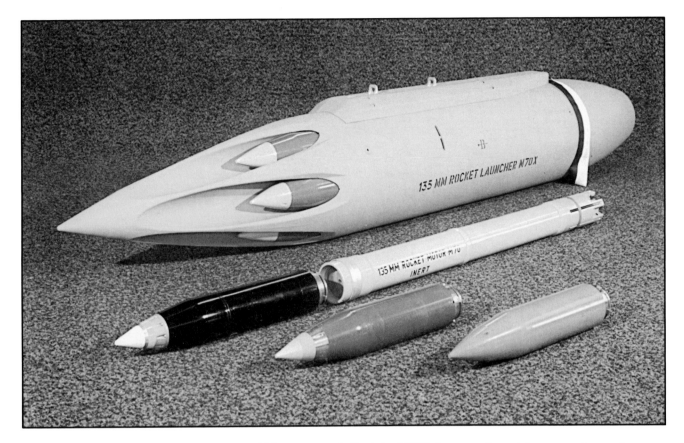

the 240 mm S-24, and reports of a new 325 mm round. Spain's **CASA** has developed pods for FFAR, the 70 mm INTA S-11, and the diminutive 37 mm INTAS-9. One of the best large-calibre rockets is reportedly Sweden's **Bofors 135 mm**, which is carried on the Viggen in six-round pods. Yugoslavia's **Krusik** makes 57 mm rockets, presumably based on the Soviet S-5, while the **Soko** aircraft factory manufactures 16-tube launchers for 57 mm rockets, and four-tube launchers for 128 mm.

Aside from the introduction of higher performance rocket motors, instanced by the CRV7 and Hydra-70 series, the main advance in unguided projectiles has been the advent of **fléchette warheads,** giving area coverage through the forward ejection of a hail of darts at a preset time after launch.

Several manufacturers now offer such warheads, but the fléchette concept may be illustrated by the **Thomson-Brandt Multidart** system, which entered production in 1987. Brandt uses a 9 mm AMV dart weighing 36.5 gm, and a 13.5 mm ABL dart weighing 187.5 gm. The 68 mm rocket will accept 36x9 mm or 8x13.5 mm darts, while the 100 mm rocket takes 192x9 mm or 36x13.5 mm. At an impact velocity of 1640 ft/sec (500 m/sec), the AMV *(anti-matériel et véhicule)* dart can penetrate 8 mm of armour, and the ABL *(anti-blindé léger)* can go through 15 mm. There have also

One of the most advanced air-to-ground rocket systems in use today is the Bofors 135 mm M70X, which is available with GP, AP/fragmentation and practice heads, and is cleared for supersonic carriage. (Bofors Ordnance)

39

been reports of a much heavier (850 gm) AB dart, of which the 100 mm rocket would carry only eight, and that will pierce 80 mm of armour, but this does not yet appear to have reached production status. These TBA Multidart rockets are typically fired at a slant range of 1600-3500 metres from a height of less than 250 ft (75 m), providing impacts over an area (depending on the type of dart) up to 1200 metres long and 40 metres wide.

Probably the largest unguided rocket in production, the 240 mm Russian S-240 is shown on the ground in front of this Peruvian Air Force Sukhoi Su-22. Other weapons on show include UV-32-57 rocket pods, FAB250 bombs, and unspecified cluster weapons. (Revista Aerea)

Chapter 3

`Dumb` Bombs and Dispensers

SECURITY RESTRICTIONS prevent the discussion of nuclear, bacteriological and chemical weapons. The following notes therefore refer only to the use of conventional types of explosives.

During the Second World War Britain's RAF emphasised the development of bombs that were suitable for both internal carriage in bombers and external carriage on fighters, plus a few very heavy and specialised bombs that were phased out as soon as the conflict had ended. The powerful fighter engines that were available toward the end of the war allowed the RAF to standardise on the use of a 1000 lb (454 kg) bomb that was a compromise between a fighter's demands for low drag and a bomber's need for high packaging density in the weapons bay. It is probably true to say that this bomb was optimised for flattening German cities, but it was equally effective in destroying mud forts, so it became the standard weapon for any scenario. Any target that was too big for a Hunter armed with 3-inch (76 mm) RPs with 60 lb (27.2 kg) warheads was hit by a Canberra with 1000 lb (454 kg) bombs.

The US services adopted a different approach, with a whole range of bombs from 250 lb (113 kg) to 3000 lb (1360 kg). It can be argued that the sheer scale of USAF and USN operations made it easier to adopt a multiplicity of bomb types. On the other hand, there is no doubt that a stick of four 500 lb (227 kg) bombs gives a far higher probability of making a cut across a runway than two of 1000 lb (454 kg). Nor is there doubt that certain hard targets (eg, steel bridges) are more affected by a direct hit from a 2000 lb (907 kg) bomb than by any number of smaller strikes. The RAF has thus been over-restricted in its HE bombs.

Right: The Saab JA 37 Viggen with its principal store options. The aircraft is armed with three 600 kg anti-ship Saab 04E missiles, and the centreline droptank is on the ground. The front row consists of 16 120 kg bombs with nose probes for enhanced anti-personnel effect. The rear row has two Sidewinders (inboard), then four Bofors 135 mm pods, two types of ECM pod, two 300 kg Saab 05A air-surface missiles, and two Falcon air-air missiles. (1 Thuresson, Saab-Scania)

If weapons can be delivered from the upper surface of an aircraft, then extremely low level attacks will be possible. This Rockwell artist's impression refers to a Low Level Weapons Delivery System (LLDS) based on the use of lifting bodies. (Rockwell International)

The first of the postwar improvements to conventional bombs was the design of **low-drag shapes** by Douglas, resulting in the US Navy LDGP (low drag, general purpose) series: the 250 lb (113 kg) (Mk 81, the 500 lb (227 kg) Mk 82, the 1000 lb (454 kg) Mk 83, and the 2000 lb (907 kg) Mk 84. These weights are nominal values, indicating only the class of weapon.

The second postwar development was the introduction of **braking systems** to provide a safe separation between the aircraft and the point of impact in the case of a low level release. Braking is generally achieved by means of a fabric parachute or metal airbrakes, the former system producing greater drag, but the latter having the advantage in terms of

The first General Dynamics YF-16B (serial 76-0751) is seen dropping what appears to be a stick of LDGP Mk 82 bombs. The aircraft is carrying an AIM-9L Sidewinder on the wingtip, and a Westinghouse ALQ-131(V) jammer pod under the wing. (General Dynamics)

Test release of a Mk 84 bomb with BSU-50/B Air Inflatable Retarder (AIR) or Ballute, from a USAF A-7D, serial 69-6194. (Loral Systems Group)

maximum deployment speed. More recently, Loral Systems has developed an **Air-Inflatable Retarder** (AIR) bomb decelerator that is based on the BALLUTE (BALLoon parachUTE) concept and makes possible the combination of high drag and deployment speeds up to 700 knots (1300 km/hr). The AIR is produced in three sizes: the BSU-49/B for the Mk 82, the BSU-85/B for the Mk 83, and the BSU-50/B for the Mk 84. In a typical delivery from a height of 200 ft (60 m) at a speed of 550 knots (1020 km/hr) in a level pass, the AIR provides the aircraft with a separation of 1375 ft (420 m) from the point of impact.

The use of metal airbrakes in the US series of retarded GP bombs is illustrated by this Mk 81 'Snakeye' with 'daisy-cutter' nose fuse. (Roy Braybrook)

Whatever the retarding system, it involves a weight penalty. Whereas the free-fall Mk 81 weighs 270 lb (122.4 kg), the retarded **('Snakeye')** version with metal brakes increases this figure to 300 lb (136 kg). The free-fall Mk 82 weighs 530 lb (240 kg) and the retarded version 570 lb (258.5 kg). The AIR systems weigh 56 lb (25.4 kg) for the Mk 82, 90 lb (40.8 kg) for the Mk 83, and 96 lb (43.5 kg) for the Mk 84. The standard British retarded 'thousand-pounder' with parachute weighs 1120 lb (508 kg).

The **Matra 2000** retardation system also uses a parachute, and was introduced in 1965 for 250 and 400 kg bombs. This was followed by the new SFA *(Système de Freinage et d'Amorçage)* retarding and arming system to extend the release envelope, suit smaller bomb sizes, and allow air bursts from extremely low altitude delivery. Fitted to the SAMP 125 kg bomb, the SFA 125 produces the **BL-61** retarded bomb, which may be released down to 75 ft (24 m) and at speeds up to 400 knots (740 km/hr). On the SAMP 250, the SFA 250 produces the **EU2** super-retarded bomb, which may be released at the same height at speeds up to 650 knots (1200 km/hr). Aside from increasing aircraft separation at impact, a retarding system also steepens the angle of the bomb's descent, thus improving the lethality of the fragmentation, most of the pieces being thrown out at right angles to the axis of the bomb. Effectiveness may be further improved by the use of an impact fuse associated with a long nose-probe, giving detonation just before the body of the bomb reaches the earth. Such weapons are often referred to as 'daisy-cutters'.

Due to the sheer size of retarder required, heavy bombs are difficult to slow down. Combining this fact with the need for a linear attack system to deal with targets such as convoys of logistic support vehicles, **Thomson-Brandt** has developed the **BAT 120** retarded bomb of only 75 lb (34 kg). Nine of these weapons on a Type 14-3-M2 adaptor weigh 728 lb (330 kg), and 18 on a Type 30-6-M2 weigh 1620 lb (735 kg), this latter arrangement being a typical centreline load for a French Air Force Jaguar.

Nine Thomson-Brandt BAT 120 lightweight retarded bombs, mounted on a Type 14-3-M2 adaptor on the outboard pylon of a Jaguar. (Thomson-Brandt)

Two types of warhead are available: the AMV that generates 2600 fragments of 4 gm, able to pierce 4 mm of steel at a distance of 65 ft (20 m), and the ABL that generates 800 fragments of 12.5 gm, capable of piercing 7 mm at the same distance. The BAT 120 may be released at speeds up to 550 knots (1020 km/hr). From a height of 260 ft (80 m) it strikes the ground at an angle of approximately 85 degrees, producing a near-horizontal hail of fragments 2.3 ft (0.7 m) deep.

Aside from achieving safe weapon release in a low level attack, the main objective in postwar bomb development has been to provide more kills with a given bombload, although recently the aim has switched to obtaining a standoff capability that allows the launch aircraft to remain outside target defences.

The basic **high explosive (HE) bomb** is a good way to destroy buildings, but its effectiveness against vehicles and personnel is limited. It has a strong casing to allow it to penetrate a concrete structure before exploding, but this casing breaks into a small number of relatively large pieces. If it lands on sand or soil, the HE bomb buries itself and then throws a narrow cone of debris into the air. The effect is spectacular, but lateral damage is severely restricted.

One alternative for low level ground attack is the **napalm** bomb, which for PR reasons is now often referred to simple as a firebomb. It consists of a droptank filled with fuel, to which is added a jelling agent and an impact fuse. Since it can be prepared literally overnight, any service

The spectacular effects of napalm (with the phosphorus igniter disappearing off-stage left) are exemplified by this picture, taken in the course of Hawker Hunter demonstrations in Switzerland. (British Aerospace)

can state that it does not stock firebombs. This type of weapon was employed in the Second World War and Korea for anti-personnel and anti-tank duties. Although a somewhat inaccurate bomb, giving only a narrow streak of fire, it is effective against troops caught in the open, and it has more psychological impact than traditional bombs. It is useful in Alpine areas at times when HE bombs would cause avalanches, though (at the opposite extreme) it is of limited value in jungle. The US Mk 77 firebomb contains 64 Imp gal (290 litres) and the Mk 79 holds 93 Imp gal (424 litres). There are now more effective ways to kill personnel (though they are all considerably more expensive), but Argentina had a stock of napalm bombs on the Falklands, and Libya is reported to have used napalm in Chad.

Fuel-air explosive (FAE) weapons operate by producing a cloud of fuel droplets, which is detonated to create a highly destructive pressure wave. Aside from killing personnel and destroying buildings, FAE weapons can be used to clear fields of pressure-activated mines, and to remove trees and other vegetation from a planned helicopter landing site. This type of armament was first used operationally in 1969 in Vietnam, when the CBU-55 was employed to clear landing zones. This cluster bomb unit weighed 500 lb (227 kg) and contained three BLU-73 bomblets, each of which reportedly weighed 100 lb (45 kg) and contained 70 lb (32 kg) of ethene oxide in fluid form. The CBU was released from a helicopter or low-speed aircraft, its case was split by detonating cord, and the bomblets then descended on parachutes, to be blown apart when triggered by a proximity fuse at a height of around 30 ft (9 m). A second minor explosion then detonated the aerosol cloud.

In 1971 the CBU-55 was supplemented by the CBU-72, which could be used from high-speed aircraft (by virtue of a braking parachute), while the BLU-73 was replaced by the improved BLU-76. The US Marine Corps introduced the MADFAE bomb with 12 propene oxide bomblets for mine clearing, and it was claimed that a single such weapon could clear a million square feet (ie, 22.5 acres or 9.1 hectares).

There are now reports of so-called second generation FAE weapons, which provide heavier warloads and higher reliability, being less sensitive to atmospheric conditions. Two such devices are the 500 lb (227 kg) BLU-95, containing 300 lb (136 kg) of propene oxide, and the 2000 lb (907 kg) BLU-96, with 1400 lb (635 kg) of fuel. This latter weapon can be delivered in several ways, including the GBU-15 glide bomb. There have also been references to a new US Navy FAE bomb in the 1000 lb (454 kg) class, using methane as fuel.

Fragmentation and Bomblets

The basic HE bomb produces a concentrated effect that is suitable for certain targets (such as bridges and hardened command and control centres), but more generally produces an overkill in a very limited area. Targets such as tanks may be destroyed by much smaller warheads, hence

there is a case for distributing the energy of the warhead over a greater area that is matched in length and breadth to the errors in the weapon delivery system. In a typical low level attack the along-track errors may well be three or four times the cross-track errors, hence in this context the best weapon may be one that spreads its effects over an ellipse or rectangle that is three or four times as long as it is wide.

The firebomb discussed earlier probably produces too narrow a coverage to satisfy this criterion. A simple fragmentation bomb presumably gives a circular coverage, which is far from optimum, but cheap. For example, the **Armscor 265 lb (120 kg)** fragmentation bomb is a low-drag shape with 60 lb (27 kg) of RDX/TNT surrounded by layers of steel balls cast in epoxy and contained in a fibreglass casing. Depending on the type of target, the bomb may be chosen to contain 42,000 balls of 6.7 mm diameter, 26,000 of 7.9 mm, 19,000 of 8.7 mm, or 15,000 of 9.5 mm. The bomb may be fitted with an airburst fuse, or an impact fuse with a delay up to 18 seconds.

One way to lengthen the ground coverage from a single weapon is to release the warhead as a series of braked modules. For example, the **Thomson-Brandt BM400** modular bomb contains three 200 lb (90 kg)

Five Thomson-Brandt BM 400 modular bombs, each containing three anti-armour submunitions, mounted on an Alpha Jet. (Dassault-Breguet)

49

cylindrical anti-armour submunitions which are withdrawn from the rear end of the casing at preset intervals by their respective parachutes. These modules descend vertically and are detonated at the optimum height by probe-mounted fuses. Two types of prefragmented canisters are available, one producing 800 fragments that can pierce 12 mm of steel at 330 ft (100 m), and another that produces 1500 fragments giving 7 mm penetration at the same distance. The BM 400 is designed to be used as a stand-off weapon, a forward toss from around 5 km allowing the aircraft to remain outside the range of most automatic fire. There have also been references to a rocket-assisted version with twice the stand-off range, and to the development of the much larger BM 1200, which will weigh over a tonne and will carry a wide variety of payloads.

An alternative approach is to use a large number of bomblets, which generally are shaped charges with secondary anti-personnel effects, and to dispense them simply by removing the bomb casing or by some more sophisticated means. This concept goes back at least as far as the Second World War, when the Luftwaffe used the 8.8 lb (4 kg) SD4HL shaped charge bomblet (a derivative of the SD2 anti-personnel bomblet) in containers holding 78.

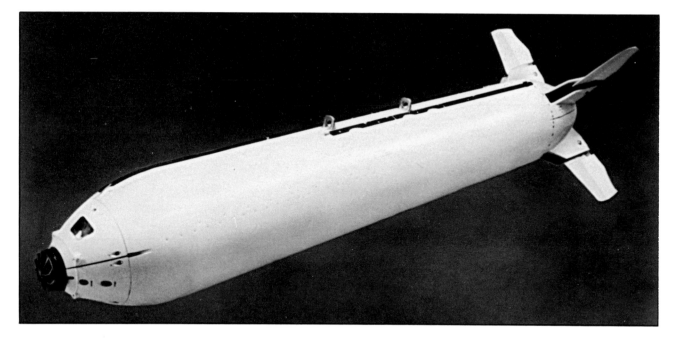

One of the most widely used CBUs (cluster bomb units) is the **Rockeye** (currently the Mk 20 Mod-IV) anti-armour cluster munition, which weighs 490 lb (222 kg) and contains 247 M118 bomblets. Released at a height of 500 ft (150 m), these bomblets typically give coverage over an area of 30,000 sq ft (2800 m²). Dispensing is provided by a linear shaped charge that splits the bomb casing at a preset time from weapon release. The main

The Rockeye anti-armour cluster bomb contains 247 bomblets and is one of the most widely used CBUs. (ISC Technologies)

international contractor for Rockeye is ISC Technologies, which company has also developed an area denial version, with 160 fragmenting submunitions preset to detonate at various times according to one of 100 different programmes.

A modern example of an anti-personnel CBU is the **Armscor CB470,** which weighs 990 lb (450 kg) and contains 40 rubber-coated spherical bomblets, each weighing 14.3 lb (6.5 kg). The bomb can be released at speeds up to 600 knots (1100 km/hr) and at heights between 100 and 1000 ft

(30-300 m). At a preset time after release from the aircraft the bomblets are ejected from the bomb by high pressure gases from a cartridge. Ground impact activates a time-delayed fuse, and the bomblets bounce (even from mud and water) to burst 0.65 seconds later at a height of 10-16.5 ft (3–5 m). The system is developed to give lethal coverage over an area 800 ft (250 m) by 230 ft (70 m). It is envisaged that an aircraft such as a Mirage F1, attacking a linear target, might drop four pairs at 0.4 second intervals, giving denser fragmentation over an area of approximately 600,000 sq ft (54,000 m²). Flight trials of the CB470 were carried out in 1985 using a Mirage F1AZ, and there are reports that this weapon (which is derived from the **Alpha** bouncing bomb used in Rhodesia in the early 1970s) has been employed operationally by Iraq in the Gulf War.

The **Matra/TBA Beluga** is officially described as a grenade-dispenser. It weighs 628 lb (285 kg) and contains 151x66 mm grenades weighing 2.65 lb (1.2 kg) each. It may be released at speeds up to 540 knots (1000 km/hr) and as low as 200 ft (60 m). The Beluga is retarded by a

The Armscor CB470 anti-personnel CBU, with its 40 rubber-coated bouncing bomblets, which detonate 0.65 seconds after impact. (Armscor)

The Matra/TBA Beluga grenade-dispenser housing 151 submunitions, and mounted on the wing-root pylon of a Mirage 2000. (Matra)

parachute, and throws out radially 19 consecutive groups of grenades, the interval between groups selected by the pilot to cover an area 130 ft (40 m) wide that is either 400 or 800 ft (120 or 240 m) long. The grenades are individually retarded and may be of three types: general purpose, delayed action, or anti-tank (able to pierce 300 mm of armour).

The standard British CBU is the **Hunting Engineering BL755,** which weighs 600 lb (273 kg) and contains 147 bomblets. At a preset interval from weapon release a cartridge jettisons the two skin segments and inflates a series of gas bags, ejecting the bomblets from the seven compartments. The bomblet warhead is a shaped charge surrounded with notched steel wire, producing up to 2000 fragments. On ejection the bomblet extends a stabilising tail and a nose probe that carries a piezo-electric crystal to give detonation at the optimum stand-off distance. Hunting Engineering has also proposed an area-denial derivative of the BL755 termed **Hades,** with 49 Ferranti HB876 minelets.

A Hunting Engineering BL755 cluster bomb being loaded by means of two manual hoists on to the outer wing pylon of a BAe Harrier at dispersal. (RAF Germany)

Several countries outside the major powers have also developed CBUs. Israel's **Rafael** produces the **TAL-2** submunition dispenser, which scatters 270-315 bomblets by means of a fin-induced spin rate, covering an area up to 540,000 sq ft (50,000 m²). Chile's **Ferrimar** produces a 500 lb (227 kg) CBU named **Avispas (Wasps),** which dispenses 248 bomblets weighing 1.43 lb (0.65 kg) each by centrifugal action. Two types of submunition are available; an area-denial version with a preset time-delay between 30 seconds and 72 hours, and a shaped charge that penetrates more than 150 mm of armour. Chile's **Cardoen** produces a range of CBUs: the 130 lb (59 kg) CB-130 with 50 bomblets, the 560 lb (254 kg) CB-500 with 240, and the 1000 lb (454 kg) CB-1000 with 450. The Cardoen bomblet weighs 1.63 lb (0.74 kg), penetrates 150 mm of armour, produces more than 500 fragments, and has an incendiary effect due to the use of zirconium in the explosive.

Since different targets require different types of bomblets or submunitions, the USAF has developed a CBU system that is based on a standard dispenser, but which can accommodate a variety of payloads and ground coverage demands. The basic load-carrying device is the **Marquardt tactical munitions dispenser (TMD),** which is designated SUU-65, has a loaded weight in the 1000 lb (454 kg) class, and can be delivered at speeds up to 700 knots (1300 km/hr) and as low as 200 ft (60 m). Marquardt is a member of the ISC Defense & Space Group.

The first application of the TMD is the **Combined Effects Munition (CEM)** or CBU-87/B, for which Aerojet Ordnance commenced low-rate

Eight BL755s carried below the fuselage of an Italian Air Force Tornado, which also has Sidewinders on the inboard wing pylons and ECM pods outboard. (Aeritalia)

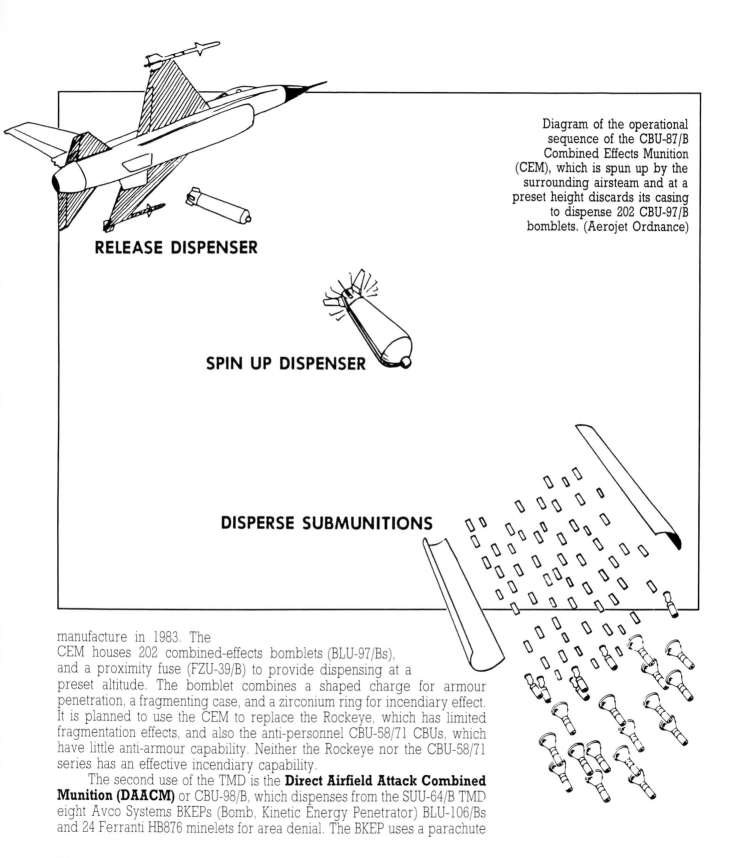

RELEASE DISPENSER

SPIN UP DISPENSER

DISPERSE SUBMUNITIONS

Diagram of the operational sequence of the CBU-87/B Combined Effects Munition (CEM), which is spun up by the surrounding airsteam and at a preset height discards its casing to dispense 202 CBU-97/B bomblets. (Aerojet Ordnance)

manufacture in 1983. The CEM houses 202 combined-effects bomblets (BLU-97/Bs), and a proximity fuse (FZU-39/B) to provide dispensing at a preset altitude. The bomblet combines a shaped charge for armour penetration, a fragmenting case, and a zirconium ring for incendiary effect. It is planned to use the CEM to replace the Rockeye, which has limited fragmentation effects, and also the anti-personnel CBU-58/71 CBUs, which have little anti-armour capability. Neither the Rockeye nor the CBU-58/71 series has an effective incendiary capability.

The second use of the TMD is the **Direct Airfield Attack Combined Munition (DAACM)** or CBU-98/B, which dispenses from the SUU-64/B TMD eight Avco Systems BKEPs (Bomb, Kinetic Energy Penetrator) BLU-106/Bs and 24 Ferranti HB876 minelets for area denial. The BKEP uses a parachute

The Avco BLU-106/B Boosted Kinetic Energy Penetrator (BKEP) with tailfins unfolded. It uses a tail parachute and rocket accelerator to achieve runway penetration prior to detonation, (Avco Systems Textron)

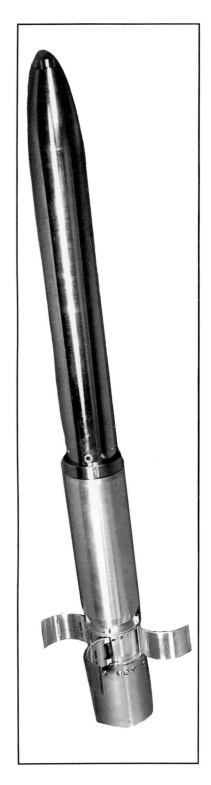

to give a steep descent, and a rocket to produce a high impact velocity, allowing the projectile to pass through the runway and explode underneath, resulting in a large area of upheaval. At time of writing both the BKEP and the DAACM are still in full-scale development. A decision for initial production is scheduled for the end of the 1989.

The third use of the TMD is the **Gator** landmine system, which is one of the FASCAM (FAmily of SCAtterable Mines) series, currently under development by the US Army's Armament Research and Development Center (ARDC). The Gator dispenser is known as the CBU-89/B in USAF use, and as the CBU-78/B with the US Navy. Each dispenser contains a total of 94 minelets, which are a mixture of anti-armour BLU-91/Bs with magnetic influence fuses, and anti-personnel BLU-92/Bs, which are activated by automatically deployed tripwires. Tactical fighters such as the F-4 can carry up to 14 Gator dispensers each, but the system is also scheduled for use by the FB-111 and B-52 on deep interdiction missions. The dispenser may be released at speeds up to 700 knots (1300 km/hr) and at heights down to 200 ft (60 m).

Before leaving the subject of the FASCAM series, it may be noted that one member of this family is the **Volcano** system for dispensing mines from a variety of low-speed platforms. In the case of the Sikorsky UH-60 helicopter, the system consists of four launcher racks, each of which carries 40 tubular mine canisters. Each tube holds a stack of five anti-tank and one anti-personnel mines, giving a total of 960 mines per aircraft. The Volcano dispenses the mines laterally from a height of 5-150 ft (1,5–45 m) and a speed in the range 5–120 knots (9–222 km/hr). By this means a minefield one kilometre long and with an average frontal density of almost one per meter can be laid in less than 17 seconds.

The various aircraft armaments discussed so far have all been 'dumb' in the sense that they are unguided, although the mines obviously have sensors to detect the approach of targets. A higher level of 'intelligence' is achieved if the submunition actually searches for a target and fires a directional warhead when pointing at it. This is the operating principle of the CBU-97/B **Sensor-Fuzed Weapon** (SFW), which is being developed by Avco Systems. In the case of the SFW, the SUU-64/B TMD dispenses 10 BLU-108/B submunitions, each of which contains four **Skeet smart warheads.** The Skeet is a squat cylindrical shape with an IR sensor mounted on the side, looking in a direction parallel to the axis of the warhead.

The submunition is turned to a roughly vertical position by a parachute, which is released as a small rocket motor reverses the descent rate and imparts a spin. The four Skeets are thrown outward, and spring-loaded arms superimpose a wobble on the spin in order to increase the search pattern of the IR sensor. On detecting the heat of a tank

Above: The Avco BLU-108/B submunition of the Sensor-Fuzed Weapon (SFW) system, with its four Skeet warheads deployed, prior to being dispensed by centrifugal force. (Avco Systems Textron)

Above right: The Avco Skeet smart warhead, combining an IR sensor (in the small tube on the right) with a shaped charge that projects a self-forging slug of high-speed metal. (Avco Systems Textron)

One form of Wide Area Mine (WAM), with sensors to detect the presence of armour and trigger the launching of an SFW to engage the target. (Avco Systems Textron)

An alternative form of WAM, in which two or three Skeets appear to be stacked vertically. (Avco Systems Textron)

Four of the tanks on fire in this aerial photograph were hit by the four Skeets dispensed by a single BLU-108/B submunition. In 1986 this impressive 'four-for-four' performance was repeated in a trial using Soviet-built T-62 tanks. (Avco Systems Textron)

engine, the Skeet fires a self-forging warhead, in which a shaped charge transforms a dish of heavy malleable metal into a slender projectile travelling at around 9000 ft/sec (2750 m/sec). This slug penetrates the thinner armour on top of the tank, often starting a fire.

The SFW is also used in the Avco Systems **Wide Area Mine (WAM),** which may be emplaced by various means, including aircraft. Once in place on the ground, the sensor system on the WAM detects, classifies and tracks targets, which are engaged by firing an SFW on a ballistic trajectory over the target from a long stand-off range. The WAM concept is derived from the earlier ERAM (Extended Range Antiarmor Munitions) programme, in which Avco worked under contract from the USAF Armament Division at Eglin AFB, Florida.

Submunition Dispensing

As discussed above, there are many types of CBU in service or under development, with submunitions of varying sophistication. These weapons provide some potential for a stand-off attack, the aircraft turning away immediately after releasing the bomb. There are, however, some advantages in dispensing submunitions directly from the aircraft: it may permit a lower attack, and it may make possible a more accurate weapon delivery.

The French companies of **Alkan** and **Lacroix** have jointly developed a low-cost system of dispensing 74 mm grenades from aircraft. The grenades (or 'cartridges') are manufactured by Lacroix or Brandt, and the launchers (which are reusable, and may be mounted internally or externally) are produced by Alkan or Dassault-Breguet. The Mirage can accommodate internally an 80-round launcher. The principal Alkan launchers for external carriage house 20, 40, or 192 rounds. The combined stores carriers developed by Dassault-Breguet take 59 rounds in the case of the CEM1, and 152 in the case of the 'grenadier' tank. This last example provides cover over an area 165 ft (50 m) wide and 6250 ft (1900 m) long. The principal grenade types are the 6.6 lb (3 kg) Lacroix CAV.314 for fragmentation (with a fuse delay to give an explosion on the rebound) and a Brandt hollow charge that can penetrate 230 mm of steel. This system can be used at speeds up to 600 knots (1100 km/hr) and as low as 100 ft (30 m).

The Alkan-Lacroix system dispenses comparatively small bomblets vertically, or at a small angle (up to 20 degrees) to the vertical to increase the width of coverage. In contrast, the **MW-1** *(Mehrzweckwaffe-Eins)* multi-purpose weapon that is to be used on German and Italian Tornadoes will dispense much larger submunitions horizontally. Developed by RTG (Raketen Technik GmbH), a joint subsidiary of MBB and Diehl, the MW-1 is a massive two-dimensional fairing that is attached to the belly of the Tornado. It consists of four 28-tube modules, which eject a total of 224 submunitions, selected to suit either armoured mechanised formations (Main Target Group 1, or MTG1) or airfields (MTG2). The MTG1 mix consists of the **KB44** shaped charge bomblet, the **MIFF** anti-tank mine, and

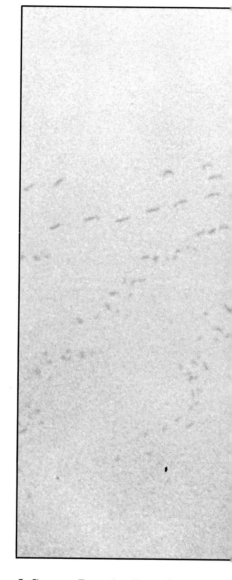

A German Tornado dispensing submunitions laterally from its Raketen Technik MW-1 belly-mounted multi-purpose weapon.
(Messerschmitt-Boelkow-Blohm)

The STABO *(STArtbahnBOmbe)* runway-piercing bomblet of the MW-1 system combines a braking parachute with a tandem warhead for maximum upheaval effect. (MBB)

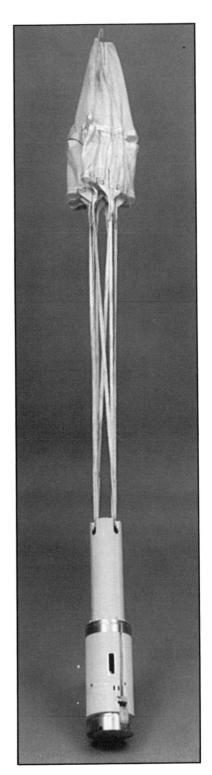

the **MUSA** fragmentation mine for semi-hard targets. The MTG2 group combines the **STABO** runway-cratering bomb, the **MUSPA** area-denial mine that detects the movements of aircraft and vehicles, the MIFF anti-armour mine, and the **ASW** anti-shelter submunition. The STABO submunition uses a parachute to steepen its descent, then a tandem warhead that uses a shaped charge to blow a hole through the paving so that the second charge can explode underneath for maximum upheaval.

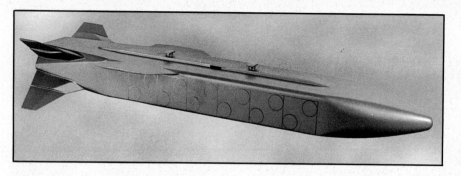

MBB's DWS-39 is a dispenser weapon system that is being developed for Sweden's JAS 39 *Gripen*. It will be released from the aircraft prior to dispensing, its stub wings providing some stand-off capability. (MBB)

Test-firing of the Hunting Engineering JP233 runway-attack system from an RAF Tornado, the Ferranti HB876 minelets falling from the forward portion, and the much larger Hunting SG357 runway-cratering submunitions from the rear. (Hunting Engineering)

Left inset: The Hunting Engineering SG357 cratering submunition, of which each JP233 houses 30, as exhibited at the SBAC Show. (Roy Braybrook)

The MW-1 is the first of a family of submunition dispensers, which either carry out their function while attached to the aircraft (and are then jettisoned) or form a stand-off attack system, being released prior to dispensing. The **Modular Dispenser System (MDS)** is made up of standard four-tube modules in which the tubes are either arranged in-line or in a square. Like the MW-1, the MDS is designed as a captive system that is jettisoned when empty. In contrast, the **DWS-39** (Dispenser Weapon System for the JAS 39) is released prior to dispensing. Several DWS-39 containers may be carried on one aircraft.

In RAF service the strike version of the Tornado is armed with the **Hunting JP233** system, which differs from the MW-1 in being intended purely for airfield attack, in being pylon-mounted, and in using downward ejection of submunitions. In addition to being responsible for system management, Hunting Engineering developed the **SG357** runway-cratering submunition. The other part of JP233 is the **HB876** area-denial submunition, which was developed by Ferranti.

The Ferranti HB876 area-denial submunition, of which each JP233 carries 215. Note the spring-loaded legs, upward-directed shaped charge, and lateral fragmentation effect. (Rex Lowden for Ferranti)

MBB's Vertical Ballistic Weapon (VBW) will take the form of pods (flown here on the inboard pylons of a German Air Force Alpha Jet), combining sensors and tube-launched munitions. (MBB)

The RAF Tornado GR1 carries two JP233 pods under the fuselage, each containing 30 SG357s and 215 HB876s, and weighing 5150 lb (2335 kg). The SG357s are carried in a vertical plane, nose-up at 30 degrees from the horizontal. They are ejected downwards by individual hot-gas systems, breaking through frangible covers in the base of the pod. They are initially stabilised by metal fins, then retarded and pitched nose-down by parachutes. Runway penetration is achieved by means of a tandem warhead, as discussed in the context of STABO. The HB876 submunitions are dispensed downwards through tubes inclined outboard at 15 degrees or 35 degrees from the vertical. They descend on parachutes, and on landing are turned upright by spring-loaded petals.

The JP233 concept is also applicable in repackaged form to other aircraft, although the F-111 would have taken four unmodified pods (ie, twice the Tornado load) under the wings. The Hunting proposal for the F-16 is equivalent to one JP233 pod, but using two smaller containers, one with 30 SG357s weighing 3020 lb (1395 kg), and the other with 215 HB876s weighing 2535 lb (1150 kg).

The use of a massive dispensing system such as the MW-1 against tanks is cost-effective when they are grouped together, but if they are dispersed on the battlefield, a different approach may be necessary. The **VBW (Vertical Ballistic Weapon)** system developed by MBB is a reusable pod containing 18 tube-launched munitions and a variety of sensors that scan the ground that is being overflown. When a tank is located, the VBW automatically attacks it with Bazooka-type weapons. The basic pod is approximately 13 ft (4 m) long and weighs 705 lb (320 kg), hence two can be carried by a small aircraft such as the Alhpa Jet.

This side-view of the VBW pod suggests that recoil loads are eliminated by firing counterweights upward as the munitions go downwards. The 27 mm Mauser BK27 that appears to be below the VBW is actually mounted on the aircraft centreline. (MBB)

Anti-Runway Weapons

Airfield attack systems such as the MW-1 and JP233 inhibit the use of runways by cratering the paving and by covering the surrounding area with mines that pose a threat to personnel, repair vehicles and aircraft. The basic idea is presumably that a very small number of heavy strike fighters can put an airfeld out of action by each making a single pass along the runway, dispensing submunitions for most of its length. If the attacking force does not possess such aircraft, or if it does not want to be restricted in the direction of its attack, then it may prefer to use larger numbers of aircraft to make a series of cuts across the runways.

Although simple HE bombs will penetrate runways in dive attacks, in low level attacks they will simply bounce off the surface. It is thus necessary to retard the bomb (which steepens its dive angle and gives the aircraft a safe separation from the impact point) and then employ some special means to penetrate the concrete. This may be done either with a tandem charge, as discussed earlier, or by using a rocket to accelerate a hard-nosed bomb to a speed that will take it through the paving. The tandem charge appears to make possible a lower bomb release, but it is probably more difficult to develop.

It can easily be demonstrated mathematically that the probability of a successful runway cut is increased by the use of relatively small bombs (for a given warload), although such weapons create more drag on the aircraft, and their small craters may well be easier to repair.

The outstanding example of the small runway cratering weapon is the

Thomson-Brandt BAP100, which weighs only 72 lb (32.5 kg) and has been adopted by the French Air Force. It is accelerated by rocket to an impact speed of over 850 ft/sec (260 m/sec) and penetrates 12 inches (30 cm) of concrete. It may be released at speeds up to 550 knots and heights as low as 215 ft (65 m). Nine BAP100s on a 14-3-M2 adaptor weigh 705 lb (320 kg), and 18 on the 30-6-M2 adaptor weigh 1565 lb (710 kg).

The **Matra Durandal** is a somewhat heavier weapon, weighing 485 lb (220 kg), but it operates on the same retard-accelerate principle. Impact velocity is 885 ft/sec (270 m/sec), and a penetration of more than 15.75 inches (40 cm) is assured. It may be released at speeds up to 600 knots (1100 km/hr) and at heights down to 250 ft (75 m). Durandal has been ordered by 14 services at time of writing, including the US Air Force.

A French Air Force Jaguar with its standard runway-attack load of 18 Thomson-Brandt BAP100 bombs on a Type 30-6-M2 adaptor on the centreline pylon. It is also carrying two 1200-litre tanks and a PhiMat chaff/flare dispenser. (Thomson-Brandt)

Above: The Matra Durandal runway-piercing bomb has been adopted by the USAF as the BLU-107/B. Durandal warhead test *(right)* on typical runway paving, apparently simulating the destruction of taxyways to hardened aircraft shelters. (Matra)

A load of eight Durandals, carried below the fuselage and wing-roots of a Mirage 2000. (Matra)

Winged Dispensers

Since several countries (notably Germany, and to a lesser extent Britain and the US) have developed families of submunitions, an obvious response to current demands for a stand-off attack capability is to propose winged dispensers to act either as glide bombs or (for longer ranges) as powered vehicles. Such attack systems may be regarded conceptually as the crossover point between 'dumb' and guided weapons, since for close support work they may function unguided or with only the crudest form of heading-hold, but for ranges of several hundred kilometres they clearly require precise dead-reckoning, and possibly some form of homing.

Several Euro-NATO nations had already begun the development of winged submunition-dispensers when in the autumn of 1986 seven countries (the US, the UK, Canada, France, Germany, Italy and Spain) began discussions on the joint development of a **Modular Stand-Off Weapon (MSOW)** series. Although the future of the MSOW programme is by no means secure, its tentative launch appears to have halted work on the US/UK/German LRSOM (Long-Range Stand-Off Missile) and the US/Canadian/Spanish/Italian LOCPOD (LOw-Cost Powered Off-boresight Dispenser). Several other systems that are still at an early stage may also be abandoned in favour of the MSOW series, hence the following discussion is limited to a few of the more significant examples.

One of the technology leaders in this field is the Brunswick Corporation's Defense Division, which in the late 1970s was funded by the USAF Armament Laboratory at Eglin AFB to develop a **Low Altitude Dispenser (LAD)** and perform a series of demonstration flights. The LAD was to be compatible with a wide variety of submunitions (six were in fact flown, and over 15 satisfactorily evaluated), to demonstrate safe separation at speeds of 325–550 knots (600–1020 km/hr), and to show the feasibility of making a stand-off attack with an unpowered dispenser from a height of less than 100 ft (30 m).

The Brunswick LAD is a rectangular-section dispenser with four aft-mounted cruciform wings, and provision for a rocket motor to offset the slow launch speed of the A-10. The loaded dispenser weighs approximately 2350 lb (1065 kg) with a 1400 lb (635 kg) payload. Targets can be attacked at 40 degrees off boresight and at ranges up to 24,000 ft (7300 m). The submunitions may be carried either parallel to the dispenser axis, or in 48 transverse tubes of 135 mm diameter, using the MW-1 system.

The **Apache/CWS (Container Weapon System)** is a joint development by Matra and MBB, aimed at an in-service date of 1992. Whereas the LAD has fixed wings of low aspect ratio, this Franco-German system has high aspect ratio wings that fold back over the fuselage for ease of carriage. The basic glider version will have a range of around 10 km, but a turbine-engined variant is also planned with a range of 50–80 km. Aside from the German submunitions developed for the MW-1, this dispenser will also carry a new family of weapons developed by Matra: the general-purpose Mimosa, the anti-tank Acadie, and the runway-piercing

Typical of the coming generation of winged stand-off submunition-dispensers, the Apache/CWS (Container Weapon System) is a joint Matra-MBB development. (Matra).

Close-up of the Apache/CWS with wings folded, mounted for flight tests below the centreline of a Mirage F1. (Matra).

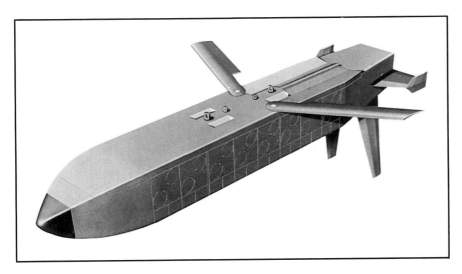

Samanta. The unpowered version is expected to weigh around 2200 lb (1000 kg) and the turbine-engined version 2650 lb (1200 kg).

A competing Franco-German development is the **MoBiDic** project, in which Aérospatiale and Thomson-Brandt are collaborating with Dornier and Diehl. In this case the French submunitions are being developed by TBA, notably the SMAP anti-runway and SMABL anti-tank weapons.

Italy's contribution to this field is the **Skyshark** dispenser that is being developed by the **CASMU** consortium of Aeritalia and SNIA-BPD, the latter company being responsible for the development of the submunitions. The

Jettison trials with the CASMU Skyshark dispenser were carried out in 1987 on this Italian Air Force Tornado.
(Aeritalia/SNIA-BPD)

two basic versions are a glider and a rocket-powered derivative, although use of a turbojet is also being considered. The Skyshark is unusual in having a somewhat rounded cross-section and delta wings, but it is in the same weight category as the Apache/CWS. Flight trials began in 1987.

As indicated earlier, some or all of these European projects may be incorporated in the seven-nation MSOW programme, which is reportedly aimed at an in-service date of 1994. Very little has been published of plans for MSOW, though press reports indicate that it may eventuate as three basic variants, aimed at ranges of 15–20 km, 30–50 km, and 185–600 km. These three versions would clearly differ in propulsion, guidance, and payload, and it remains to be seen if they could have a significant degree of commonality. The MSOW programme nonetheless appears to offer the prospect of reducing duplication in the field of NATO R&D, and of a worthwhile gain in armament standardisation.

Chapter 4

Air - Surface Guided Weapons

THE FUNDAMENTAL ADVANTAGE of a guided missile over simpler forms of weapons as discussed earlier, is that it can deliver a heavy warhead accurately at long range. It follows that guided weapons first came into use in the context of high-value, heavily-defended 'hard' point targets such as warships, bridges and dams. Guided weapons, however, could achieve military significance only when avionics had progressed to a useful level in the fields of VHF/UHF radio, airborne radar, TV, etc. Thus, although some primitive guided weapons were projected as early as the First World War (the 'Kettering Bug' surface-surface cruise missile flew in 1918), the guided missile did not really amount to anything serious until the Second World War.

The first realistic air-surface guided weapons were Germany's anti-ship rocket-powered Henschel Hs 293 and the Fritz-X glide bomb, which were deployed operationally in 1942 and 1943 respectively, both using radio command guidance. The **Hs 293** was the lighter of the two, weighing 1730 lb (785 kg) at release, and delivering a 1120 lb (500 kg) warhead, generally against large merchant vessels. The **Fritz-X** or FX-1400 weighed 3400 lb (1540 kg) and was designed as an armour-piercing bomb for use against warships. This missile's greatest success came on 9 September 1943 in a surprise attack by Dornier Do 217K-2s of KG100 against ships of the Italian Navy, which were steaming to Malta to join the Allied forces. The Dorniers were mistaken for friendly aircraft, hence there was no defensive fire, and the battleship *Roma* was sunk (two hits produced a fire that blew up the main magazine) and her sister-ship *Italia* was damaged by a single hit.

In subsequent attacks on Allied warships supporting the amphibious landings near Salerno (just south of Naples), the Fritz-X and Hs 293 together sank six ships and damaged 10 more, including the RN battleship *Warspite* and the cruiser *Uganda,* and the USN cruiser *Savannah.* Fritz-X was also employed with some success to destroy bridges over the River Oder, to slow the advance of Russian forces. The Germans experimented with TV control for the Hs 293D in October 1944, and with the **Blohm und Voss BV 246** glide bomb, which was basically an anti-radar missile (ARM), but neither of these projects saw operational service.

Although the **V-1 (Fieseler Fi 103 or FZG-76)** was a relatively heavy weapon, weighing 4730 lb (2145 kg) at launch, a number were fired against England from Norwegian-based He 111Hs, in order to overcome the 150 nm (280 km) range restriction and the loss of ground-launch sites just across the Channel. The V-1 carried a 2200 lb (1000 kg) warhead and used simple dead-reckoning navigation (ie, preset heading and time to fuel cut-off), though a TV guided version was projected.

The Japanese, although desperate to sink US carriers in the Pacific, lacked the technology to develop GW, so flew suicide missions with bomb-laden aircraft of various types. In order to improve the chance of success and reduce the cost of the 'manned missile', they also developed the rocket-powered, air-launched **Yokosuka MXY-7** *Ohka* (Cherry Blossom), which weighed only 4720 lb (2140 kg). Dropped from a Mitsubishi G4M2e Betty twin-engined bomber, the *Ohka* accelerated to 535 mph (855 km/hr), but it could still be destroyed by proximity-fused AAA fire, and its range of only 48 nm (88 km) often allowed the Betty to be intercepted by standing patrols before it could launch. On the occasion of the *Ohka's* début on 21 March 1945, all 16 parent aircraft and half of the 30 Zero escorts were shot down by a wing of more than 50 Hellcats well outside its firing range.

Although employed mostly as a surface-surface weapon, the Fieseler Fi 103 or V-1 was also launched from He 111s. An example is shown here with the much larger V-2, outside the RAF Museum at Hendon. (Roy Braybrook)

It is believed that the only homing missile employed operationally during the Second World War was the **ASM-2 Bat** developed by the USN Bureau of Ordnance for use against Japanese shipping. Equipped with a 1000 lb (454 kg) warhead and radar homing, the Bat was a glide bomb with a range of up to 8.5 nm (16 km).

Both the US and Germany made use of radio-guided unmanned bombers that were loaded with explosives and employed against specially difficult targets. In the former case stripped-down, time-expired B-17s and B-24s nicknamed 'Weary Willies' were armed with a ton of explosive and taken into the air by a pilot who baled out, the aircraft then being flown at its target by radio control from a chase aircraft. This technique was used against V-2 launch sites, but reportedly not with any great success.

The Germans used a somewhat different approach, with the guiding aircraft initially carried on the pilotless bomber in a pick-a-back arrangement. The missile was generally a modified Junkers Ju 88, and the guiding aircraft was either a Messerschmitt Me 109 or a Focke-Wulf FW 190. The intention was that the pilot of the fighter would release the bomber at some distance from the target, and would then employ radio command guidance to ensure a direct hit, but reports indicate that the only system used operationally omitted the 'Beethoven' radio link and relied simply on the fighter jettisoning the bomber at point-blank range on a direct heading for the target. Although crude in the extreme, some of the key bridges over the Oder were denied to the Russians by this *Mistel* (Mistletoe) project.

In the early postwar period there was little money available in the West to continue with the GW developments begun during the war, although some work was done on command guidance in the form of wire-guided anti-tank missiles. Such weapons were first employed operationally by French Army helicopters in Algeria firing the **SS.10** against insurgent emplacements in the early 1950s. On the same timescale the US Navy was feeling the need for an air-surface GW to attack bridges in Korea, a demand that led to the command-guided Martin Marietta AGM-12 Bullpup in the late 1950s.

It is probably accurate to say that guided missiles really came of age in the 1960s with first generation weapons such as the Bullpup, which in 1967 was augmented by the TV-guided **Martin Marietta AGM-62 Walleye.** By 1965 the anti-radar **Texas Instruments AGM-45 Shrike** had been introduced, and the **North American Hound Dog** cruise missile was in service with SAC. Britain's own nuclear strike weapon was the rocket-powered **Blue Steel** missile, carried by the Vulcan bomber.

Although not an air-launched weapon, the **SS-N-2 Styx** demonstrated the missile threat to shipping in October 1967, when three Egyptian (FPB-launched) weapons sank the Israeli destroyer *Eilat,* and triggered the development of a whole generation of helicopter-launched guided weapons that could destroy an FPB from outside the range of its defensive fire.

France led the world in the development of helicopter-launched wire-guided anti-tank missiles, the SS.10 being used operationally in Algeria in the early 1950s. Shown here is the somewhat later AS.12, giving this Alouette III the destructive power of a 155 mm gun. (Aérospatiale)

The Avro Blue Steel, seen here on its transporter at the RAF Museum, provided the Vulcan bomber with a stand-off nuclear strike capability. (Roy Braybrook)

Brazil's Embraer EMB-312 Tucano
(the third development aircraft,
PP-ZDK), armed with (circled)
Avibras twin 7.62 mm machine
gun pods on the inboard pylons.
(Avibras)

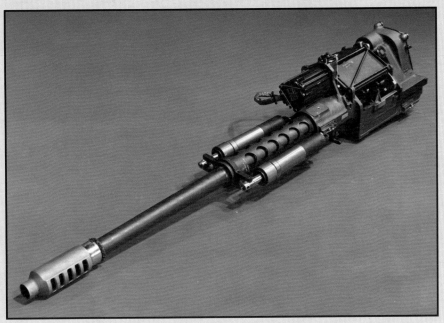

The McDonnell Douglas
Helicopter Company 30 mm M230
Chain Gun, developed
specifically for the AH-64A
Apache attack helicopter, for
which it provides suppressive
fire. (McDonnell Douglas)

The right-hand PCAP (pitch-compensated armament pylon) of
the Sikorsky H-76 Eagle is shown here fitted with the GIAT
20 mm M621 cannon pod inboard, and a Hughes Aircraft M261
19-tube 2.75-inch rocket pod outboard. This phase of weapons
trials was completed at Mojave, California early in 1987. (GIAT)

The most important new gun to
employ the Gast principle is
General Electric's 25 mm GE 225
Lightweight Gun, which is being
developed for use on
helicopters, boats, and ground
vehicles. It fires the Bushmaster
family of ammunition at a rate
that is variable up to 2000
rd/min. (General Electric)

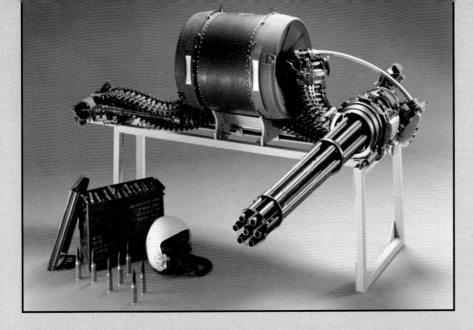

The Vulcan gun installation for the F-16, with the storage drum mounted transversely across the fuselage, feeding the M61A1 cannon in the left wing root. A linkless feed system is employed, an endless conveyor belt transporting live rounds to the gun, and returning spent cases and any unfired rounds to the far end of the storage drum. (General Electric)

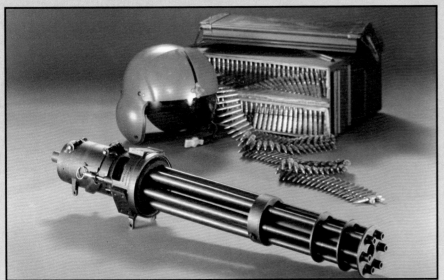

The 7.62 mm GAU-2B/A Minigun is employed on a wide range of aircraft from the Cessna AT-37 to the AC-119 gunship. Its six barrels provide a cyclic rate of up to 6000 rd/min. (General Electric)

Due to the limitations of the 7.62 mm Minigun in providing suppressive fire for helicopters, GE is now developing the 12.7 mm GECAL-50 in three- and six-barrel versions, with a rate of fire up to 8000 rd/min. This new gun will also have provisions to fire a controlled burst of around 10 shots at 4000 rd/min. (General Electric)

These spectacular results were produced by firing the 70 mm Hydra-70 rocket from Hughes M261 pods on the outboard pylons of this H-76 Eagle helicopter. (Sikorsky)

This Mirage F1 is firing 68 mm Thomson-Brandt rockets with Multidart *flèchette* warheads from four 18-round Type 155 pods. The aircraft is also armed with Matra Magic air-air missiles on the wingtips. (Thomson Brandt)

Inset right: America's early postwar 5-inch HVAR is still in use today. These four examples are shown under the left wing of an Embraer EMB-312 Tucano. (Embraer)

Inset for right: A view of an air-ground rocket firing from the launch aircraft, in this case photographed from the rear seat of an Aermacchi MB-339, looking through a Saab gunsight. (Aermacchi)

The 270 knot (500 km/hr) maximum speed of Argentina's IA-58 Pucara appears to have permitted the use of helicopter-type unfaired 2.75-inch rocket pods, as evidenced by this Falklands momento photographed at RNAS Yeovilton. Note also the twin machine gun pod under the centreline. (British Aerospace)

Inset: The Armscor 120 kg fragmentation bomb warhead, shown in sectioned form, with 27 kg of RDX/TNT, and layers of steel balls cast in epoxy between the explosive and the outer fibreglass skin. The bomb can carry 15,000-42,000 balls, and can have either an impact fuse or a proximity fuse for airburst. (Armscor)

British Aerospace's Hawk Demonstrator (ZA101, and formerly G-HAWK) with a centreline 30 mm Aden gun and a load of Spanish EXPAL bombs. Each of the four wing pylons carries one BR500 and one BR250, which are respectively similar to the US Mk 83 and Mk 82. (Geoffrey Lee, BAe)

This burning tank was a moving target, engaged by Avco's Sensor-Fuzed Weapon (SFW) system in a test at the China Lake US Navy Weapons Center. (Avco Systems Textron)

The MBB-Matra Apache/CWS winged submunitions dispenser, currently being developed for stand-off air-ground attacks against targets such as airfields and armour concentrations.

The MW-1 multi-purpose dispenser, mounted below the fuselage of a German Air Force Tornado, which also carries a Philips BOZ-100 chaff/flare dispenser under the right wing and an AEG-Telefunken Cerebus II jammer on the left. (MBB)

Although capable of being carried by light aircraft such as the Alpha Jet, the MBB Vertical Ballistic Weapon (VBW) system has also been tested on this F-4F Phantom. (MBB)

The Avco DAACM (Direct Airfield Attack Combined Munition), partly sectioned to show its eight BL-106B penetrators (forward) and 24 HB876 minelets (aft), housed in the SUU-64 Tactical Munitions Dispenser. (Avco Systems Textron).

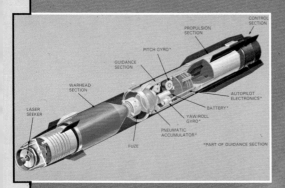

Sectioned drawing of the
AGM-114A Hellfire.
(Rockwell International)

Release of two Matra 1000 kg
laser-guided bombs from a
Jaguar. (Matra)

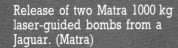

The third-generation Paveway III laser-guided
bomb is shown here on a USAF F-4C (serial
64-0930). Developed to permit operation in
Europe's bad weather and a high threat
enviroment, Paveway III allows for a variety of
release modes, including low level stand-off and
dive attacks up to 60 degrees. (Texas
Instruments)

A US Navy pilot checks the AGM-65F Maverick on the wing pylon of his A-6. The yellow band indicates a 136 kg penetrator/blast warhead. Maverick variants with a 57 Kg shaped charge warhead feature a black band. (Hughes Aircraft)

Test firing of an AGM-65 Maverick from the LAU-117/A launcher rail under the wing of an F-20 Tigershark. (Northrop)

Launch of a HOT-2 from a French Army Gazelle (Euromissile)

The first overseas sale of the AGM-88A HARM is to Germany, for use on the Tornado, with deliveries from late-1987 to 1989. This Tornado is equipped with HARMs and a Westinghouse ALQ-101 jammer pod. (Texas Instruments)

This F-4G Wild Weasel (serial 69-0263) from the 37th TFW at George AFB is carrying (from right tip to left) an AGM-45A Shrike, an AGM-78 Standard, a centreline tank, a Westinghouse ALQ-119 jammer pod, an AGM-65B Maverick, and an AGM-88A HARM. (McDonnell Douglas)

A Dassault-Breguet Mirage 2000 emerges from its hardened aircraft shelter, armed with two AM.39 Exocets and two Matra Magic air-air missiles. (Aérospatiale)

Final assembly line for the AGM-86B Air-Launched Cruise Missile (ALCM). Note the hard-edged nose of this 'stealth'-improved version. (Boeing Aerospace)

The AIM-9L Sidewinder is currently the main armanent of the RN's Sea Harrier, although AMRAAM should take over at a later stage. Sidewinder is shown here as a twin-round installation on the outboard pylon of an 899 Sqn aircraft, side number 715. Serialled XZ455, it carried the number 12 during the Falklands conflict, and was responsible for the destruction of a Mirage and a Dagger. (Philip Boyden, British Aerospace)

A rare shot of a Hunter of the Sultan of Oman's Air Force, armed with the AIM-9P Sidewinder on a special pylon ahead of the main undercarriage. (Peter Scott, Rolls-Royce)

The Armscor V3B missile (the domestic version of the export Kukri) on the wingtip of a Mirage F1AZ (serial 224) of No 1 Sqn (as indicated by the unit badge on the fin). (Armscor)

Firing of a Sky Flash from a Tornado F2 (ZD941), based at No 229 OCU, RAF Coningsby. (Flt Lt Chris Allan, via British Aerospace)

This French Air Force Mirage 2000 from EC.1/2 *'Cigognes'* is armed with two Matra Super 530Ds inboard and two Magic 2 missiles outboard. (Dassault-Breguet)

An artist's impression of the Hughes/Raytheon AAAM. (H & R Company)

The Standard ARM was developed from the RIM-66 ship-to-air missile, shown here with tandem booster. (General Dynamics)

The Styx affair was of great importance in GW development during the 1970s, but the Vietnam War (1965–75) was of even great significance. In 1968 the **General Dynamics AGM-78 Standard** ARM entered service, augmenting the Shrike. In 1972 the US Army responded to a North Vietnamese offensive involving 600 armoured vehicles, by taking out of storage some old French **SS.11s** and firing them from helicopters. The result was not a success (partly because the platforms lacked stabilised sights), so the new **Hughes BGM-71 TOW** missile system, which was then being demonstrated in Germany, was flown to Vietnam for use on the UH-1B. Two of these Hueys were fitted with XM-26 sights and fired 89 TOWs in the course of this action. Of these, 73 hit, and every hit was a kill. The helicopter-launched anti-tank GW had arrived.

That same year marked the end of the bombing halt over North Vietnam, during which the Communists had rebuilt their logistic network, and the US had developed **guided bombs** (electro-optical and laser-guided) to a far more significant level. In a three-month period during 1972, the F-4s of the 8th TFW destroyed 106 bridges in North Vietnam by the use of these weapons, including some that had defied hundreds of sorties with conventional weapons.

Using LGBs and Pave Nail (ie, with a laser designator on an OV-10

First used in Vietnam in 1965, the AGM-45 Shrike ARM was still in operational use in 1982, when it was employed by RAF Vulcans attacking Argentine radars on the Falklands. (Texas Instruments)

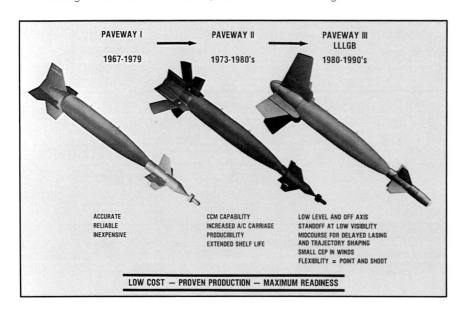

The three generations of Paveway laser-guided bombs. (Texas Instruments)

Bronco) F-4s attacking near Quang Tri in May 1972 used five LGBs to destroy four tanks in an action that lasted only six minutes! It was estimated that once the technique had been perfected, 100 typical targets in Vietnam could be destroyed by 100 LGBs, or by 4000 'dumb' bombs with computer release, or approximately 21,000 such with simple manual release.

The ending of the Vietnam War made the Middle East the new proving-ground for weapons systems. The **Shrike** ARM had already been tested by Israel in 1967 (the Six-Day War) and 1973 (Yom Kippur), and there were reports that both Shrike and the **General Dynamics Standard** ARM were employed in the 1982 invasion of the Lebanon (Operation Peace for Galilee). The more advanced **Texas Instruments HARM** first saw active service in 1986 in the course of Operation Prairie Fire, when units of the US 6th Fleet were sent into waters claimed by Libya. When SA-5s were fired against F-14s, a section of A-7s launched a total of four HARMS at the missile base on the Libyan coastline, though with only short-term results. During the subsequent Operation El Dorado Canyon strikes against Libyan bases in the Tripoli and Benghazi areas, F/A-18s and A-7Es launched a total of 30 HARMs and 12 Shrikes against ground radars. Some of the F-111Fs attacking from Britain each carried four 2000 lb (907 kg) Texas Instruments **GBU-10 Paveway 2** laser-guided bombs, although the Pentagon report also referred to a precision-guided 500 lb (227 kg) bomb.

Shrike was used from the RAF Vulcan during the Falklands/Malvinas conflict of 1982, in two strikes against Argentine radars close to Stanley. Two of these missiles fired against the main Westinghouse radar only served to put it out of operation for 24 hours, but two rounds fired later at a Contraves Skyguard radar destroyed it completely. The Paveway LGB was also used successfully late in the fighting. The conflict in the South Atlantic, however, was notable (in the present context) mainly for the use of anti-ship missiles. This began during the retaking of South Georgia with the firing of eight old **AS.12** wire-guided missiles from two RN Wasp helicopters against the Argentine submarine *Santa Fé*. This had earlier been depth-charged by a Wessex and was consequently running on the surface. The boat took four AS.12s in the conning-tower, but limped back to Grytviken, where it sank alongside the jetty. The next air-surface missile to see service was the **BAe Sea Skua,** which was deployed with the Lynx helicopter. The first firings came in a night-time engagement, when two Lynxes launched four rounds at the patrol boat *Alferez Sobral,* which was badly damaged but managed to get back to Argentina. A few weeks later two Lynxes fired four rounds at the cargo vessel *Rio Carcarana,* previously damaged by Sea Harriers and naval gunfire. Two missiles hit and started a fire, and the ship later sunk. A ninth Sea Skua was fired just before the Argentine surrender at the patrol vessel *Rio Iguazu,* which had been damaged and beached. This round exploded in the superstructure, causing additional damage.

The conflict thus provided useful operational trials for the brand-new Sea Skua, but it also served to validate the effectiveness of the Aérospatiale **AM.39 Exocet,** which armed Argentine Navy Super Etendards. In the first strike two AM.39s were fired against the destroyer *Sheffield*. Only one hit, but it started fires in fuel tanks amidships, and the vessel had to be abandoned. A few weeks later two were fired against the container ship *Atlantic Conveyor,* and on this occasion both hit, starting a fire that destroyed it. The fifth and last air-launched Exocet available was fired in a later attack but missed, probably because of chaff and helicopter-borne radar decoys. It is of technical interest that two MM.40 Exocets were fired from land sites against the destroyer *Glamorgan*. One hit and again started a fire, but the ship was well prepared for such a strike. The fire was extinguished, and *Glamorgan* remained available for action.

The AM.39 has also been used extensively by Iraq throughout several years of the Gulf War with Iran, which began in 1980. Air attacks on tankers began in March 1984, Iraq using the AM.39 from Mirage F1s and Super Etendards, while Iran used the AS.12 and **Hughes AGM-65B Maverick** from F-4s. The most commonly used missile appears to be the AM.39, but only a small proportion of attacks have led to actual sinkings, since strikes are generally well above the waterline, and the warhead has not always exploded. In early 1985 the use of radar decoys was introduced, further reducing the Exocet's kill-rate.

This outline of the history of air-surface GW serves to make the point that this category of armament has been able to play a significant military role for at least a quarter-century, and that tactical air-ground missiles for both fixed- and rotary-wing aircraft, anti-radar missiles, and anti-ship missiles have all been employed operationally. In the cruise missile category Western products have never been fired in anger, but it is believed that both Egypt and Iraq have used the **AS-1 Kennel** (against Israel and Iran respectively), and it is possible that Iraq has also employed the **AS-5 Kelt,** a rocket-powered derivative of the turbojet-powered AS-1.

The following sections discuss the various present-day air-surface GW categories in more detail.

Tactical Air-Ground GW

The simplest form of air-surface GW is the guided bomb, since this can be produced merely by adding a homing head and control surfaces to an existing low-cost weapon. Such a weapon can achieve very small miss distances, and it may allow the parent aircraft to make a toss attack from behind cover. Stand-off range may be extended by the use of flip-out fins, and (if necessary) by the addition of a rocket motor. Guidance is normally provided by laser-homing, IR-homing, or TV contrast-lock, though Northrop is now working on inertial guidance.

It is estimated that around 25,000 smart bombs of various types were used in Vietnam, beginning in 1968. The most important guided bomb was the **Texas Instruments Paveway** LGB, which was normally released from an F-4 at altitude in the approximate direction of the target, while the observer in another F-4 illuminated the target with a cockpit-mounted stabilised Martin Marietta AVQ-9 laser designator. The LGB was generally dropped in a 30 degree dive, a height of 16,500 ft (5000 m) giving a stand-off distance of perhaps 5 km. The Pave Knife system placed the stabilised designator in an underwing pod, so that the launch aircraft could mark its own targets. Paveway II includes large folding fins, making the system suitable for bombs up to Mk 84 size, and providing greater

accuracy. For British use, Texas Instruments developed a Paveway version of the Mk 13/18 1000 lb (454 kg) bomb. Target illumination may be provided by a coded laser on the launch aircraft or an aircraft from the same flight, a helicopter, or by the FAC on the ground. Over 150,000 Paveway modification kits have been supplied to 15 operators.

Various Paveway improvements are under development. The **GBU-24 Paveway III** has much larger fins and two-stage guidance, and is intended to provide longer stand-off range from a low level delivery. Reports indicate that only the 2000 lb (907 kg) version will be purchased, and that development options include a rocket motor and imaging infra-red (IIR) or millimetre wave seeker.

The French equivalent of the Paveway series is the **Matra LGB,** developed in conjunction with Thomson-CSF, who are responsible for both the ATLIS laser designator pod and the EBLIS laser detector on the bomb. The system may be applied to bombs in the range 250–1000 kg, the heaviest weapon being designated *Arcole*. It is claimed to have a range of more than 5 km, and a terminal accuracy better than 5 metres. As currently envisaged, the Matra LGB family will consist of general purpose 250 kg and 400 kg weapons, the latter being very suitable for attacking ships, and penetration bombs of 400 kg and 1000 kg, the latter being developed to meet a French Air Force requirement for a weapon to demolish bridge piers.

At the Paris Air Show of 1987, Israel Aircraft Industries unveiled its own LGB, designated **Guillotine.** It is claimed that this new weapon uses technology superior to that of its predecessors, giving a glide range of up to 30 km from a launch height of 40,000 ft, and an accuracy of 2 metres CEP. There is considerable flexibility in regard to delivery mode, and the navigation system is designed to ensure a steep impact angle, to take

An RAAF Mirage IIIO, armed with three Paveway IIs, two of which are carried on forward hardpoints on the auxiliary tanks. Note the other attachment points and sway-bracing on the tanks, and the ARDU badge on the fin. (Texas Instruments)

Above: Matra's 1000 kg 'Arcole' BGL *(Bombe Guidée par Laser),* carried on the inboard wing pylon of a Mirage F1. The 'Arcole' was developed specifically to meet the needs of France's FATAC *(Force Aérienne TACtique)* in regard to the destruction of bridge piers. (Matra)

Above Right: The Elbit Opher is a low-cost IR-homing terminal guidance kit, which is intended to be used in conjunction with a modern weapon-aiming computer on the aircraft. It thus requires the minimum degree of 'smartness', and eliminates the need for target illumination. (Elbit)

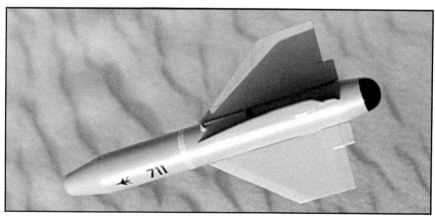

Israel Aircraft Industries' 'Guillotine' laser-guided bomb was unveiled at Le Bourget in 1987. (IAI)

The Rafael Pyramid is a TV-guided glide bomb with a Mk 82 warhead. The black dielectric cover at the rear houses the antenna for the data-link that transmits the TV picture back to the launch aircraft. (Rafael)

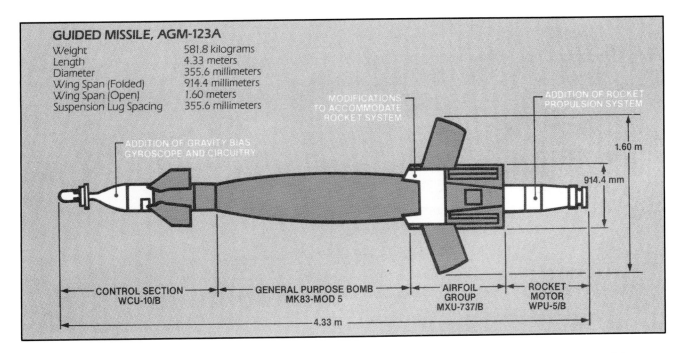

GUIDED MISSILE, AGM-123A

Weight	581.8 kilograms
Length	4.33 meters
Diameter	355.6 millimeters
Wing Span (Folded)	914.4 millimeters
Wing Span (Open)	1.60 meters
Suspension Lug Spacing	355.6 millimeters

MODIFICATIONS TO ACCOMMODATE ROCKET SYSTEM

ADDITION OF ROCKET PROPULSION SYSTEM

ADDITION OF GRAVITY BIAS GYROSCOPE AND CIRCUITRY

1.60 m

914.4 mm

CONTROL SECTION WCU-10/B

GENERAL PURPOSE BOMB MK83-MOD 5

AIRFOIL GROUP MXU-737/B

ROCKET MOTOR WPU-5/B

4.33 m

General arrangement of the AGM-123A Skipper II. (Emerson Electric)

advantage of the thin armour on top of a tank.

Another Israeli system is the **Elbit Opher** low-cost IR terminal guidance kit, which is described as bridging the gap between dumb bombs and conventional smart weapons. In essence, the bomb is released using a modern weapon aiming computer, and initially falls ballistically. At a distance of about 1000 metres from the target (eg, a tank), the homing head senses the thermal radiation and corrects the trajectory to provide a direct hit. The Opher thus exploits the capability of the aircraft system, and uses only the minimum 'smartness' to achieve the desired result. Since laser illumination is not required, there is complete flexibility of delivery mode, and the minimum aircraft exposure to target defences.

A third new Israeli guided bomb shown at Paris in 1987 was the **Rafael Pyramid,** described as a low-cost TV-guided glide bomb. Based on a Mk 82 warhead, the Pyramid is effectively a missile with cruciform delta wings, weighing somewhat less than 880 lb (400 kg). A data-link antenna in the base of the missile provides the launch aircraft with a picture from the TV camera in the nose, via a small communication pod on the aircraft. Pyramid is a private-venture by Rafael, giving a fire-and-forget capability from a low level toss at say 6.5 nm (12 km) range and a CEP of less than 3 ft (1.0 m). From altitude, stand-off range is sufficient to take the aircraft outside the range of the SA-5 or Patriot.

As air defence systems progress, there are increasing demands for stand-off attack capability, hence glide bombs are now being developed with rocket motors. The first such weapon to reach production status was the US Navy's **AGM-123A Skipper II,** which was devised at China Lake Naval Weapons Center in California in 1980, was tested in 1984, and was first delivered in mid-1985. Skipper II is currently manufactured by Emerson Electric, and is basically a laser-guided Mk 83 Paveway II with the

Test firings of AGM-123A Skipper II guided missiles from a Grumman A-6A Intruder, serial 155592. (Emerson Electric)

rocket motor from the Shrike ARM, produced by Aerojet Tactical Systems. It is reported that the missile will also be built by Texas Instruments.

The US Air Force is following a similar line of development with the **GBU-15,** based on the Mk 84 warhead. The story of this modular guided bomb goes back to 1973, when Rockwell was appointed prime contractor for its development, with Hughes Aircraft responsible for the AXQ-14 data-link. The resulting GBU-15 Cruciform Wing Weapon (CWW) weighs 2450 lb (1140 kg) and in its initial version has TV-guidance. The homing head may be locked on to the target before or after launch, the data-link providing in the launch aircraft a visual image of the target, and a means for the pilot to steer the CWW manually. An alternative homing head (WGU-10/B) based on imaging-IR is available in the GBU-15(V)2/B, the TV-version being the (V)1/B. Indirect delivery is the normal method of attack, relying on the data-link to provide target acquisition during flight, but aircraft not equipped with the data-link pod can use the GBU-15 in a direct attack mode, with lock-on prior to launch and automatic guidance.

For use in the defence suppression role, the Mk 84 warhead may be replaced by a CBU-75 cluster warhead, essentially an SUU-54 dispenser with BLU-63 submunitions. Flight trials of the TV-version began in 1975, followed by those of the IIR version in 1982. The GBU-15 is credited with being suitable for delivery from less than 200 ft (60 m), and with ranges in excess of 5.0 nm (9.25 km).

The **Rockwell AGM-130A** is basically a GBU-15 with a rocket motor attached below the warhead, increasing the low level firing range to

This photograph of an F-111 shows late-model GBU-15s with the wings and canards of the AGM-130A. (Rockwell)

around 13 nm (24 km) and the launch weight to 2917 lb (1323 kg). In order to optimise the toss distance attainable, the AGM-130 has an altimeter for height control. Reports indicate that it also has a new data-link by Harris-Magnavox. The guidance and warhead options appear to be unchanged from the unpowered GBU-15. The boost motor is jettisoned at burnout.

The latest trend in the field of guided bombs is the provision of night and all-weather capability, which is reportedly to be a feature of **Paveway 4.** There is also some concern regarding the ability of even the standard Mk 84 warhead to destroy a really hard target, hence the development of an upgraded Mk 84, termed the **hard target munition (HTM).** Before leaving the subject of guided glide bombs, it should be recalled that the projected Modular Stand-Off Weapon (MSOW), as mentioned at the end of the previous chapter, also belongs in this category, although the emphasis is on excellent glide performance and submunitions dispensing, and some form of propulsion is planned from the outset.

Turning to more conventional guided weapons, one of the most widely used of tactical air-surface missiles is the **Hughes Aircraft AGM-65 Maverick** series, which range in weight from 462 lb (210 kg) up to 675 lb (307 kg). Maximum firing range is in the region of 10 nm (18.5 km), but target acquisition limitations generally restrict firings to around half this figure. The **AGM-65A** is TV-guided, the pilot simply selecting the target on his cockpit display, placing crosshairs over it, and firing the missile, which

Note: as this book went to press it was reported that both the AGM-130 and Skipper programmes had been deleted from the Fiscal Year 89 budget.

Four versions of Hughes Aircraft Maverick: from front to rear, the USAF IR-guided AGM-65D, the USMC laser-guided AGM-65E, the TV-guided AGM-65B (now in production for overseas sales), and the USN imaging-IR AGM-65F. (Hughes Aircraft)

This tank is about to be struck by a Hughes Aircraft AGM-65E laser Maverick.

is guided by TV lock-on. The **AGM-65B** is an improved version with scene-magnification, providing acquisition at longer range. These first two variants saw active service in Vietnam and the 1973 Middle East War.

The **AGM-65D** features IIR homing, using the same sensor as the GBU-15(V)2/B. It is not all-weather, since IR cannot see through clouds and rain, but it does provide a night capability, and it can see through the smoke of battle. Target acquisition is normally possible at 5–6 nm (9–11 km), which is twice the range attainable with TV. The AGM-65D's digital centroid seeker takes the missile to the centre of the target, rather than the hottest point. The 125 lb (57 kg) shaped-charge warhead of the earlier models is retained.

The USMC **AGM-65E** employs laser-homing for precise delivery in the close support role, and a 300 lb (135 kg) blast-fragmentation warhead. The US Navy **AGM-65F** combines this heavier warhead with the IIR seeker of the -65D, although the guidance system is modified to suit a ship target, giving a hit at the middle of the ship, just above the waterline. In trials over 85 per cent of Mavericks have scored direct hits, and of the 100 fired in actual combat 87 achieved hits.

The **Aérospatiale AS.30L** is a much heavier laser-guided weapon, weighing 1145 lb (520 kg) at launch, and carrying a 530 lb (240 kg) warhead at supersonic speed (Mach 1.5) over a distance of up to 5.4 nm (10 km). Flight control is by thrust vectoring, and terminal homing combines TV-tracking and target identification and laser homing. In attacks on bunkers, the warhead can pierce 6.6 ft (2 m) of concrete before exploding, and its CEP is given as less than 3.3 ft (1.0 m). Other types of target include bridges, hardened aircraft shelters, and ships. Over 500 AS.30Ls have been ordered, including 180 for the French Air Force.

This Jaguar is armed with two Aérospatiale AS.30L laser-guided missiles, and has an ATLIS guidance pod on the centreline. (CEV Cazaux)

A great deal of Western armament plans are concerned with defeating large numbers of enemy tanks. Ideally, NATO would have aircraft that could make effective attacks against a number of scattered point targets during a single pass, notwithstanding the latest armour developments. Aside from the complexity of simultaneously guiding rounds against individual targets, it is known that reactive armour (which explodes when struck by a missile) defeats conventional warheads. Some existing GW types are therefore being fitted with tandem warheads, the first to set off the reactive armour and the second to penetrate the conventional armour beneath it. However, this is not the only possible solution.

The **Hypervelocity Missile (HVM)** system being developed by Vought would allow an aircraft to engage up to 10 individual targets in a single pass, using missiles carrying kinetic energy warheads, probably making use of depleted uranium (DU) rods. The USAF version of the HVM is planned as a 66 lb (30 kg) projectile of 3.8 inches (96.5 mm) calibre,

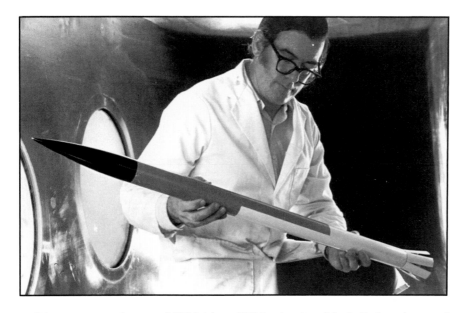

The Vought HVM (HyperVelocity Missile) is a command-guided projectile that will enable an aircraft to engage up to 10 targets in a single pass. (Vought)

striking at a speed around 5000 ft/sec (1500 m/sec) or Mach 5. An advanced FLIR sensor on the aircraft will track both the targets and missiles, and transmit guidance commands over a carbon dioxide laser data-link. Through the use of synchronous clocks, the missiles will recognise their own signals, and change their courses by firing jets of gas through small nozzles in their forward sections. Firing range is approximately 2.2 nm (4.0 km). Despite its sophistication, the HVM system should be inexpensive to operate, as the missile itself is very simple. A cost of $8300 in FY85 terms has been estimated for the projectile.

Little is known of Soviet tactical ASMs, beyond the fact that the principal models are the radio-guided AS-7 Kerry, the laser-guided AS-10 Karen, the AS-12 Kegler, and the AS-14 Kedge.

Helicopter-borne ATGW

The most widely used anti-tank guided weapon (ATGW) is the **Hughes Aircraft BGM-71 TOW** (Tube-launched, Optically-tracked, Wire-guided) missile, with over 300,000 delivered to more than 35 nations. Development began in the early 1960s, at which stage the US Army required a range of only 2000 metres. The current maximum range is 3750 metres.

Prototype firings took place in 1965, demonstrating the remarkable CEP of only 1.6 ft (0.5 m). Production deliveries began in 1969 and the system was operational in the following year. In the Vietnam War a total of 162 TOWs were fired from helicopters, and 124 of these scored hits. The missile was also used during the Yom Kippur War of 1973, with a success rate of over 90 per cent. As for most first generation ATGW, the TOW works on the SACLOS (Semi-Automatic Command to Line-Of-Sight) principle, with the gunner holding his sight on the target, and an IR sensor tracking a flare carried by the missile. Corrective signals are fed down wires that are dispensed from the base of the missile. A thermal imager is available for night engagements.

Improved TOW (ITOW) has a spring-loaded telescopic nose-probe for optimum stand-off distance, and a more effective warhead, although the diameter remains unchanged at 5 inches (12.7 cm). The next stage of development is **TOW-2,** which is heavier and carries a 6-inch (12.25 cm) warhead. It also has an improved propellant with a 30 per cent greater impulse, offsetting the higher weight of this variant. Tests are being carried out on the use of a secure radio command guidance link to replace the existing wires, and deliveries have begun of a TOW-2A with a small warhead on the nose-probe to detonate the target's reactive armour. There have also been references to FITOW (Further Improvements to Tow), with a proximity fuse and an advanced warhead, to give an over-the-top attack capability. Thorn EMI Electronics leads a development team consisting of Royal Ordnance, Hughes Aircraft amd Westland Helicopters.

The **Euromissile HOT,** jointly developed by Aérospatiale and MBB, is claimed to be the most powerful weapon in its class. More than 70,000 have been ordered, and at the start of 1987 a total of 8713 had been test-fired, with a kill rate of 91.4 per cent. Maximum range is 4000 metres, and HOT-2 carries a warhead of 5.9 inches (15 cm) diameter, capable of piercing up to 1300 mm of armour. Also available is a multi-purpose warhead consisting of a hollow charge surrounded by a thick fragmenting casing.

Euromissile is now developing an ABA warhead that is designed to defeat reactive armour consisting of a layer of explosive sandwiched between two light armour plates. When struck by the high energy 'dart' from a shaped charge warhead, the reactive armour explodes, throwing the top plate outward at high velocity. Since the missile generally hits at an acute angle, the 'dart' meets a constantly renewed armoured surface, which destroys it before it can reach the main armour of the tank. The ABA warhead will use two hollow charges in tandem, the first to neutralise the reactive armour, and the second to pierce the main plating. Other

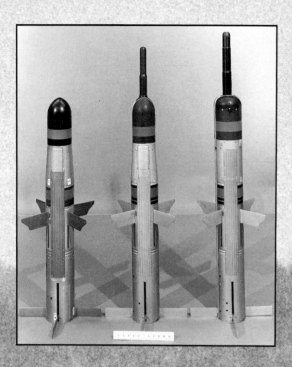

The sequence of developments of the Hughes Aircraft BGM-71 series is shown in this photograph, with the original TOW on the left, Improved TOW in the centre, and TOW-2 on the right. (Hughes Aircraft)

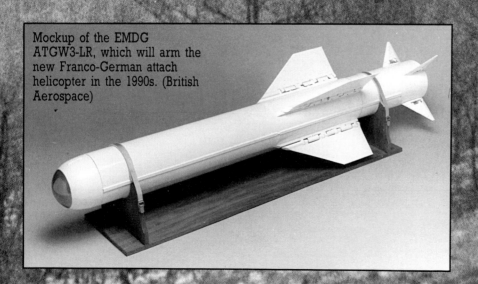

Mockup of the EMDG ATGW3-LR, which will arm the new Franco-German attach helicopter in the 1990s. (British Aerospace)

Firing of a Euromissile HOT from an Aérospatiale Gazelle. (Euromissile)

The ATGW3-LR with wings and tailfins folded for loading in its launch-tube. (MBB)

developments include the Viviane day/night thermal imaging sight, which is expected to supersede the current APX M397 day sight.

In the mid-1990s HOT is scheduled to be replaced by the third-generation **ATGW3,** developed by the EMDG consortium, combining Aérospatiale, MBB, and British Aerospace. This new weapon is to be produced in two versions, for medium and long ranges. The ATGW3-LR will be used from vehicles and helicopters, and the latter variant is to be developed with MBB as prime contractor. Range is increased to 4500 metres, and SACLOS guidance will be replaced by IIR homing, with a terminal dive attack. The use of a homing missile will make possible a high rate of fire, and permit the launch helicopter to take evasive action immediately after firing. The ATGW3-LR is expected to equip the Franco-German CATH (Common Anti-Tank Helicopter), formerly known as the PAH-2 / HAP / HAC-3.

The US Army regards its **Rockwell AGM-114A Hellfire** (Helicopter-launched, fire-and-forget) weapon as a third-generation missile. Hellfire is operational with the Army's AH-64 Apache helicopter, and in AGM-114B form (with safety modifications to suit shipboard operation) is being used by the USMC on the AH-1J SeaCobra and AH-1W SuperCobra. Possible future applications include the OV-10, AV-8B, and F/A-18 fixed-wing aircraft.

Not a pretty sight! A US Army AH-64A Apache attack helicopter, armed with 16 Hellfire missiles and a chin-mounted 30 mm M230 Chain Gun. (McDonnell Douglas Helicopter Co.)

Hellfire is a relatively large missile, weighing 95 lb (43 kg) at launch, compared to 44 lb (20 kg) for TOW and 51 lb (23 kg) for HOT. Its size is explained by the fact that it cruises supersonically and carries a large warhead of 7 inches (17.8 cm) diameter. The basic US Army requirements were for multiple target engagements, day/night and adverse weather capability, extended range, short flight time, high single-shot kill probability, and indirect fire capability (eg, from behind a hill, with lock-on after launch). These demands are currently met through the use of laser homing, the target having been marked either by the launch aircraft or another designator, although future options include millimetre wave active radar, IIR, and a combined RF/IR seeker. The Improved Lethality Hellfire Program is introducing EOCM, a digital autopilot, and provisions for trajectory tailoring to suit particular tactical applications and avoid low cloud.

The standard Russian helicopter-launched ATGW are the wire-guided **AT-3 Sagger,** which is used on the Mi-2 and Mi-8, and the **AT-2 Swatter,** which has been seen on the Mi-8 and Mi-24, and is believed to have some form of terminal homing. The latest Soviet weapon in this series is the **AT-6 Spiral,** which equips some models of Mi-24, is launched from a tube, and is thought to have radio command guidance.

Anti-Radar Missiles

The suppression of enemy air defences (SEAD) is a multi-faceted operation, involving radar and communications jamming, attacks on AAA and SAM batteries (generally with CBUs), the use of artillery fire against forward air defence units, and attacks by anti-radar missiles (ARMs) from specially-equipped aircraft, which in the USAF are referred to as 'Wild Weasels'.

The first significant ARM was the **Texas Instruments AGM-45A Shrike,** which was developed by the US Navy Weapons Center at China Lake, and entered service in 1964. Based on the AIM-7 Sparrow air-air missile, Shrike carried a 145 lb (66 kg) blast/fragmentation warhead over a range of up to 22 nm (40 km). It was a useful first generation ARM, but it had a single frequency seeker, which was preset to suit the planned target. It thus lacked operational flexibility, and it had no memory of target position, hence it could be defeated by switching off the transmitter. Shrike was nonetheless used in Vietnam and the 1973 Yom Kippur War against SA-2 sites, and during 1982 by Britain in the Falklands and by Israel in the invasion of the Lebanon.

The **General Dynamics AGM-78 Standard** ARM is a much heavier weapon, weighing up to 1800 lb (816 kg) at launch. It entered production in 1968, and provided a major improvement over Shrike in terms of range and warhead size, and in having a broad-band seeker and memory circuitry to enable an attack to be continued successfully after transmitter shutdown. An Israeli-modified AGM-78 is code-named 'Purple Fist', and has reportedly been used against Syrian radars.

Above: The latest US anti-radar missile is the Texas Instruments AGM-88A HARM, shown here mounted on an F/A-18 Hornet (Texas Instruments)

Above right: Both versions of the Anglo-French Martel missile are shown here on the wing pylons of a BAe Buccaneer, namely the anti-radar version on the left and the TV-guided version on the right. (British Aerospace)

The **Texas Instruments AGM-88A HARM** (High-speed Anti-Radiation Missile) was developed during the 1970s by China Lake, to replace both the Shrike and Standard ARMs. It is believed to be suitable for attacks on a wide range of radar categories, and to have three firing modes: 'self-protection' (cued by an ALR-45 radar warning receiver), 'pre-briefed' to carry out a post-launch search for a specific radar, and a 'target-of-opportunity' mode. Cruise speed is reportedly in the region of Mach 2.5. The AGM-88 entered service in 1984, and was used in US Navy strikes against Libyan coastal defences in 1986.

The first major European ARM was the Anglo-French **AS.37 Martel,** developed jointly by Hawker Siddeley and Matra in the 1960s, with deliveries beginning in 1971. Martel was produced in both ARM and TV-guided versions, and the former remains in service with British and French forces (the TV missile being used only by the RAF). It is said to have been used by French forces in 1987 operations in northern Chad, though without any notable success. Martel was considered for use by RAF Vulcans against Argentine radars on the Falklands, but this plan was abandoned in favour of the use of Shrike.

Matra has undertaken the unilateral development of an improved anti-radar missile named **ARMAT** (Anti-Radar MATra) derived from Martel, offering increased range and other advantages, possibly in the fields of radar signature and flight speed. Reports indicate that Iraq has used this weapon operationally in the Gulf War, firing from a 'Wild Weasel' variant of the Mirage F.1EQ.

Firing of the anti-radar Matra ARMAT from a Mirage F1. (Matra)

The **BAe ALARM** (Air-Launched ARM) is a dedicated defence-suppression missile, being developed to meet RAF AST.1228 to equip the Tornado GR1 and possibly other British ground attack aircraft. Its modes of operation include a climb followed by a descent on a parachute, searching for enemy radar transmitters. For this role, ALARM was selected in preference to HARM, which was chosen for the German Tornado ECR variant.

The trend appears to be toward complementing a sophisticated ARM such as HARM or ALARM with a much smaller weapon, which ground attack aircraft can carry in addition to their primary armaments. There were plans for a seven-nation Short-Range ARM **(SRARM),** but at the time

Test-firing of the BAe ALARM from a Tornado. (British Aerospace)

British Aerospace mockup of a possible configuration for the Short-Range Anti-Radar Missile (SRARM). (BAe)

of writing this project has been halted by the sudden withdrawal of America in mid-1987 due to economy reasons. The US Navy is already developing a short-range self-protection ARM in the form of the **Motorola AGM-122A Sidearm**. The intention appears initially to be to defend USMC helicopters such as the AH-1J SeaCobra against front-line AAA, notably the ZSU-23-4 Shilka, though later Sidearm would equip fixed-wing aircraft such as the AV-8B and OV-10D. There have also been references to a **Dual-Mode Maverick,** which would initially be steered by inputs from the radiating target, but could complete the attack using TV lock-on.

Matra is developing a relatively light-weight ARM named **STAR** (Supersonic Tactical Anti-Radar), which will weigh about 440 lb (200 kg), and will be powered by a Matra-ONERA ramjet. This new weapon will be used by the Super Etendard and Rafale D/ACE to attack air defence radars and punch holes in SAM networks so that strike units can penetrate.

The next stage of ARM development involves the use of much longer loiter times, which can be attained only through the use of turbine engines. The **Northrop AGM-136A Tacit Rainbow** project is the first such weapon, providing a sustained, long-range search and attack capability both in the air-land battle and in maritime operations. This weapon will be carried internally by the B-52G and externally by aircraft such as the A-6E. Flight

The Northrop AGM-136A Tacit Rainbow features a straight wing that is set below the fuselage and pivots through 90 degrees for ease of stowage in the weapons bay of a B-52G. After launch, it loiters, searching for enemy radars to attack. (Northrop)

trials began in 1986 and are due for completion in 1988, when a low-rate initial production decision is anticipated.

As in other air-surface GW categories, very little is known of Soviet ARMs, but it is generally accepted that the AS-9 Kyle, AS-12 Kegler, and possibly the AS-11 have capabilities in this role.

Anti-Ship Missiles

Any of the ARMs discussed above can be employed against naval vessels, with a view to putting out of action their search and fire control radars, and possibly causing casualties in the bridge area. If the aim is completely to disable and possibly sink the target, however, then a different type of weapon is required, that will blow a large hole in the target below or on the waterline.

There are two principal types of anti-ship missiles: those intended to destroy an FPB, (usually lightweight weapons fired from a helicopter), and much larger weapons that may disable almost any type of ship. There are, however, several missiles that appear to fall between these categories.

The broad requirements in developing an anti-ship missile are to strike from outside the range of the target's defences, to have a guidance system that (ideally) provides a day/night all-weather fire-and-forget capability, to give the target the least chance of detecting (and thus destroying) the missile, and to damage the target catastrophically.

The range required in attacking an FPB appears to be in the region of 8–16 nm (15–30 km), depending on the sophistication of the target. An attack on a single large vessel would require a missile range of at least 25–50 nm (45–90 km), and a strike against a member of a carrier battle group suggests a launch from the radar horizon at medium level, ie 200 nm (370 km). The limited range associated with an attack on an FPB can be achieved with a rocket motor, but the current trend is to use air-breathing engines (turbines or ramjets) for all the new weapons in the larger categories.

All-weather autonomous operation suggests active radar guidance. The small radar that can be accommodated by a missile has a number of operational limitations, however, notably in its ability to deal with 'clutter'. Active radar missiles thus have difficulty in attacking a target located between islands, or anchored in a fjord. In the 1982 Falklands conflict, one of the considerations behind the choice of San Carlos Bay for the British landing on East Falkland was that Exocet could not attack the ships while they were unloading in the bay.

It was in order to overcome this limitation that the British Aerospace Sea Skua was given semi-active radar guidance, although this requires the launch aircraft to continue to illuminate the target throughout the flight-time of the weapon. Command guidance (as used in the case of the AS.15TT) is one alternative, but is difficult to make compatible with ripple firing, since each weapon requires its own coded signals. It was specifically to permit attacks on landing craft operating in fjords that Norway's Kongsberg Penguin has IIR guidance, though this does not provide full all-weather capability.

The probability of successfully penetrating the target's defences depends on achieving the lowest possible sea skimming height and the highest possible speed (in order to give the shortest warning time). In first generation anti-ship missiles the sea-skimming height is preset according to sea conditions. For example, in the case of Exocet it can apparently be varied from 26 ft (8 m) down to 10 ft (3 m). Second generation weapons are more sophisticated. In the case of the BAe Sea Eagle, the missile computes the wave height from the output of a very accurate radar altimeter, and adjusts its sea-skimming height accordingly. In the case of the BAe Sea Skua, the sea-skimming height is reduced in a series of steps as the target is approached, coming down extremely low as it enters the firing range of the CIWS. In order to increase the chance of defeating the ship's defences, some next-generation missiles will use a supersonic cruise, although this clearly implies a significant range penalty.

Turning to the matter of terminal lethality, ie, the chance of a kill in the event of a direct hit, the aim is to explode a large warhead after a deep penetration, hence the missile must not bounce off the side of the ship, and it must be sufficiently rugged to survive the penetration of an armoured hull.

The lightest of the anti-FPB missiles is the **Aérospatiale AS.15TT,** which equips the SA.365F Dauphin 2 helicopters of the Royal Saudi Navy. Automatic command guidance, based on the Thomson-CSF Agrion radar of the Dauphin, was adopted to provide all-weather capability, compatibility with confined waters, and a low-cost projectile. The AS.15TT is reported to have a weight of 212 lb (96 kg) at launch, and to deliver the old AS.12 66 lb (30 kg) warhead over a range of 8 nm (15 km).

The fact that the AS.15TT has failed to sell to other countries may suggest that its performance does not match the capabilities of the FPBs of the 1990s. In addition, it is known that Aérospatiale is studying with MBB the design of a lightweight supersonic anti-ship missile designated **ANL** *(Anti-Navire Léger),* in response to a request from the German Navy, which proposes to use it on both helicopters and maritime patrol aircraft. It is anticipated that the ANL will weigh approximately 440 lb (200 kg), and will carry a 110 lb (50 kg) warhead over a 16 nm (30 km) range at a speed of Mach 2 +, using a solid-fuel ramjet. It will use inertial navigation, with active radar homing for the terminal phase.

The British equivalent of the AS.15TT is the **BAe Sea Skua,** which employs semi-active radar homing in conjunction with the Ferranti Sea Spray radar of the naval Lynx helicopter. The Sea Skua is reported to have a maximum range of around 10 nm (18.5 km), and it has certainly been more widely accepted than the AS.15TT. Aside from being used on RN Lynxes, it is also used on Lynxes of the Brazilian Navy, on German Navy Sea Kings, and on the AB.212ASWs of one other NATO navy.

Perhaps surprisingly, the US Navy appears to have given little thought to the development of lightweight helicopter-borne missiles to defend against GW-armed FPBs, although fixed-wing aircraft will use the **Hughes AGM-65F Maverick** with IIR guidance, as mentioned earlier. On current plans the USN LAMPS-III (Light Airborne Multi-Purpose System) or Sikorsky S-60B Seahawk will employ the **Kongsberg Penguin Mk 3**, a comparatively large missile weighing 820 lb (372 kg) at launch.

The Penguin began as a ship-based anti-invasion defence system, becoming operational with the Royal Norwegian Navy in 1972, when it was

British Aerospace Sea Skua
anti-ship missiles on a Westland
Lynx. (BAe)

A coastal minesweeper trials target, shown after direct hits by two BAe Sea Skuas fired from RN Lynx helicopters. The hulk sank shortly after this photograph was taken. (British Aerospace)

Homing Head

Moving Control Wing

Sustainer Motor

Warhead and Safety Arming Unit

Gyros and Gas Bottle

Control Wing Motor Actuators

Altimeter

Homing Head Electronics

Electronic Pack

Boost Motor

Left: Interior of the BAe Sea Skua. (BAe)

Far left inset: This Aérospatiale SA.365F Dauphin 2 is equipped with four of the company's AS.15TT missiles and the Thomson-CSF Agrion 15 radar. (Aérospatiale)

113

the West's first fire-and-forget anti-ship GW. The initial production models (the Mks 1 and 2) had analogue systems, but could be programmed in azimuth to follow a dog-leg course, and had a range of 14.5 nm (27 km). The **Penguin Mk 2 Mod 7** was developed for helicopters, specifically the SH-60B. It has digital systems, a two-stage motor (booster and sustainer), folding wings by Grumman, and a range of 16.2 nm (30 km). The **Penguin Mk 3** is being developed for fixed-wing applications (the RNoAF F-16), and has smaller unfolding wings, a new sustainer rocket, and a range of 21.5 nm (40 km). In addition to the dog-leg provisions of the Mk 2, the Mk 3 can be programmed in the vertical plane to clear terrain, then switch to a sea-skimming mode. All variants have a combination of inertial navigation and terminal IIR homing, plus the 265 lb (102 kg) Bullpup warhead. The effectiveness of the Penguin Mk 3 is enhanced by the use of a fuse from the Harpoon missile.

Kongsberg Penguin Mk 3 on a Royal Norwegian Air Force F-16. (Kongsberg)

Other missiles in broadly the same weight class as the Penguin are Italy's **Oto Melara Marte** and Israel's Gabriel series. The Marte Mk 1 is used on Italian Navy SH-3Ds, and Aermacchi proposes to use the active radar Mk 2 on the MB-339K. The **IAI Gabriel III** is the largest of the series and is a comparatively heavy weapon, delivering a 330 lb (150 kg) warhead over a distance of more than 32 nm (60 km), and has provisions for mid-course target update. Cruise altitude is approximately 66 ft (20 m), but in the terminal phase it is set to descend to 13, 8, or 5 ft (4.0, 2.5 or 1.5 m). The Gabriel IV is a projected long-range GW with a mid-course update facility and a turbojet engine.

The best-known anti-ship missile is the **Aérospatiale AM.39 Exocet,** as used by Argentina in the Falklands and by Iraq in the Gulf War. Aside from the sinking of the *Sheffield* and *Atlantic Conveyor* in 1982, the best-documented Exocet attack was that on the US Navy frigate *USS Stark* on 17 May 1987 by an Iraqi Air Force Mirage F.IEQ. Two missiles struck the unprepared vessel, which had been mistaken for an Iranian ship, and, although one failed to explode, some 37 crewmembers were killed and a further 21 were wounded.

Exocet has a two-stage solid rocket motor, giving a cruise speed of Mach 0.93 and a range of 27–38 nm (50–70 km) depending on the altitude and speed of the launch aircraft. It uses a combination of inertial navigation and terminal radar homing, and is credited with a warhead of 365 lb (165 kg). Over 2500 Exocets have been delivered to the navies of 26 countries, but most of these weapons are the ship-ship MM.38/40 variants. The AM.39 is used by Argentine and French Navy Super Etendards (some of the latter having been loaned to Iraq in the mid-1980s pending availability of the Mirage F.1EQ), by Abu Dhabi Super Pumas, French Navy Atlantics, by French, Iraqi and Libyan Super Frelons, and by Pakistani and Peruvian Sea Kings.

Oto Melara Marte Mk 2 on the Aermacchi MB-339B. (Aermacchi)

In view of Aérospatiale's many years of collaboration with MBB on Euromissile weapons, it is perhaps surprising that the German company has developed its own **Kormoran** anti-ship missile to meet *Marineflieger* requirements for a weapon for the F-104G (and later the Tornado). It may

Firing of an AM.39 Exocet from an unidentified (possibly Iraqi) Mirage F1. (Aérospatiale)

The MBB Kormoran anti-ship missile, mounted on a German Navy F-104G Starfighter. (MBB)

The Super Lynx, equipped with the folding-wing Kongsberg Penguin Mk 2 Mod 7 and 360-degree chin-mounted radar. (Westland)

As is true for many anti-ship missiles, the IAI Gabriel III may be launched from either aircraft or surface craft. (Israel Aircraft Industries)

Sectioned illustration of the Kongsberg Penguin. (Kongsberg)

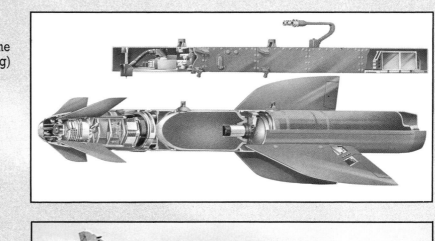

The AM.39 Exocet on a Dassault-Breguet Super Etendard. (Aérospatiale)

Below:
Launch of a Kormoran from an F-104G. (MBB) *see overleaf*

be conjectured that the German demands were more exacting than their French equivalents. It is known, for instance, that Kormoran is required to be capable of a launch as low as 100 ft (30 m). It then descends to around 65 ft (20 m), and in the terminal phase drops to between 16.5 and 6.5 ft (5.0 and 2.0 m) above the wave tops. The Kormoran warhead weighs 353 lb (160 kg) and contains 123 lb (56 kg) of explosive. Aside from producing a massive pressure wave, the warhead was designed to eject 16 large high-velocity fragments (presumably in the manner of self-forging slugs), that would hole adjacent bulkheads. Kormoran is also used by the Italian Air Force. It is understood that MBB is now producing the improved **Kormoran 2,** which, although of the same size and shape (and approximately the same weight) as the original, has longer range, a larger warhead, a digital databus, and a modified nose (to further improve the chance of armour penetration).

The moment of impact, as the Kormoran strikes the target vessel. (MBB)

As indicated earlier, long ranges demand air-breathing engines, and in the case of subsonic missiles this normally means turbojets or turbofans. The leading anti-ship GW in this category is the **McDonnell Douglas AGM-84 Harpoon,** which equips the US Navy A-6E, P-3C, F/A-18 and S-3B, the US Air Force B-52G, and the RAF Nimrod. Like Exocet, Harpoon also exists in ship and submarine-launched versions. The only known operational use of this missile occurred at the end of March 1986, when (following the firing of SA-5s against F-14s flying off the Libyan coastline) as A-6 used two Harpoons to sink a Libyan patrol boat. The air-launched version of Harpoon weighs 1145 lb (519 kg) at launch, and is powered by a Teledyne CAE J402 turbojet of 660 lb (300 kg) thrust. It carries a 488.5 lb (221.6 kg) blast warhead over a distance of more than 70 miles (130 km). The original production model uses a pop-up

A pair of McDonnell Douglas AGM-84 Harpoons, carried by an F/A-18A Hornet. (McDonnell Douglas)

manoeuvre to attack the thinner armour of the decks, but later versions provide the option of a very low sea-skimming approach. Orders for Harpoon currently stand at more than 4900 units. In any major confrontation, Harpoon would be employed in conjunction with noise-jamming, strikes by tactical aircraft, and the use of the Standard ARM and the Tomahawk cruise missile. It is estimated that two Harpoon hits would be required in the case of a destroyer, four for a cruiser, and five for a helicopter carrier such as the *Moskva* or *Kiev*.

Britain's **BAe Sea Eagle** was designed as a replacement for the TV-guided Martel, and to provide a significant advance over the French Exocet in terms of range, target discrimination, and terminal lethality. Its warhead is larger than that fitted to any of its Western contemporaries. The

Six Harpoons on a single underwing pylon of a B-52G. (McDonnell Douglas)

Internal layout of the BAe Sea Eagle missile. (British Aerospace)

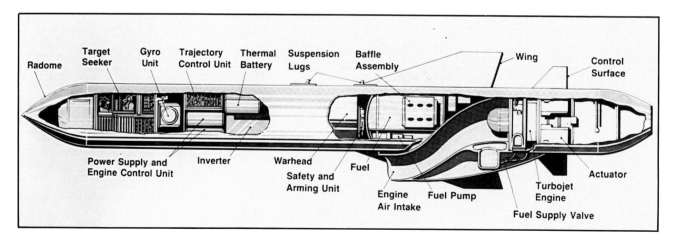

Sea Eagle weighs 1325 lb (600 kg) at launch, and is powered by a Microturbo TRI-60 turbojet of 787 lb (357 kg) thrust. It uses a combination of a pre-planned approach path (missiles fired in a single salvo striking from different directions) and active radar terminal homing, a Marconi J-band equipment acquiring the target at over 16 nm (30 km). The Sea Eagle is operational with RN Sea Harriers and RAF Buccaneers, and has also been purchased (with tandem booster) for Indian Navy Sea Kings.

The release of a Sea Eagle with external boost motors from an Advanced Sea King. The background has been revised by an artist, presumably to conceal the location of the trial, and it is not clear whether this was a jettison test or a firing. (Westland)

The Swedish equivalent of Sea Eagle is the **RBS15F,** developed by the Saab-Bofors Missile Corporation (SBMC), and powered by the same TRI-60, though in this case the engine is rated at 831 lb (377 kg). The RBS15F is essentially an air-launched version of the weapon developed for Swedish *Spica* torpedo boats by SBMC, with the external boost motors deleted. There have also been reports of an RBS15G glide bomb with TRI-60 removed, for use on the JAS 39 and AJ 37. In this case the radar homing system by Philips would be replaced by TV or IIR, although the FFV warhead would presumably be unchanged.

Some indication of the possible form of next-generation anti-ship missiles is provided by the **ANS (Anti-Navire Supersonique)** being developed jointly by Aérospatiale and MBB. The ANS will cruise at over Mach 2, powered by a solid fuel ramjet. In addition to the short warning time associated with a high speed attack, the task of the defences will be increased by its reduced radar signature and its ability to make 15g manoeuvres during the terminal attack phase. The ANS combines a

The County-class guided missile destroyer *Devonshire* was used as a target for a Sea Eagle firing trial, and suffered extensive damage from a direct hit. In operational circumstances this would have resulted in the complete disablement of the ship. (British Aerospace)

strapdown inertial navigation system and active radar terminal homing. It is expected to have a launch weight in the region of 2095 lb (950 kg), a warhead of around 400 lb (180 kg), and a maximum range of approximately 100 nm (185 km).

An artist's impression of the Swedish RBS15F missile in sea-skimming mode. (Saab-Scania)

Mock-up of the Aérospatiale/MBB *Anti-Navire Supersonique* (ANS), which is accelerated by rockets, then cruises on ramjet engines. (MBB)

Torpedoes

The massive torpedoes that submarines use to break the backs of major warships are far too heavy for aircraft to carry, but lightweight, short-range ASW torpedoes are fully compatible with both fixed-wing and rotary-wing aircraft.

Having established the approximate position of the submarine, the aircraft launches the torpedo, which is usually equipped with a parachute to control the angle of entry and the speed of impact. On entering the water, the parachute is jettisoned and the torpedo pulls out of its dive. Mid-course guidance is generally based on target data previously provided by the launch aircraft, with terminal homing provided by passive and/or active sonar. One exception is Sweden's **FFV Ordnance Tp43XO,** which requires no parachute, and combines wire guidance from the launch aircraft with sonar terminal homing.

In the past, electrically-driven (ie, battery-powered) torpedoes have been credited with a maximum speed of around 35 knots (65 km/hr) and a maximum range of 7.5 nm (14 km), the limited speed suggesting a forward hemisphere attack. Some sources credit the Soviet *Alfa* class of attack submarines with a submerged speed of more than 40 knots (74 km/hr) and the ability to reach depths greater than 1000 metres. A torpedo with a thermal engine can reach speeds of up to 55 knots (102 km/hr) and ranges of up to 25 nm (46 km). This at first sight is the obvious solution to the all-aspect attack problem in the context of high-speed submarines, although open-cycle thermal engines suffer in performance at depth due to back-pressure on the exhaust.

In recent years the **Honeywell Mk 46** has become in effect the Western standard lightweight ASW torpedo, with over 20,000 produced. The RN has employed the Mk 46 Mod 2 (replacing the **Mk 44**), but instead of the Mk 46 Mod 5 NEARTIP (NEAR-Term ImProvement) bought the **Marconi Sting Ray.** Designed to fulfil NASR.7511, Sting Ray is promoted as the most advanced lightweight ASW torpedo in the world. It entered service in 1985 with RAF Nimrods and RN Sea Kings and Lynxes, and was subsequently purchased by the Egyptian Navy and Royal Thai Navy.

The special features of Sting Ray are that:
a) it is effective in shallow water, although it has also been used successfully below 1000 metres.
b) it has a shaped-charge warhead to penetrate the thickest hull.
c) its rudders operate in the prop-wash, giving a fast pull-out from a steep entry, and excellent manoeuvrability.
d) it employs frequency-modulated sonar to counter countermeasures
e) it has a very advanced, high capacity digital computer, which stores and analyses acoustic data on several contacts and establishes target priorities.

Sting Ray may be regarded as the first of a new generation of lightweight ASW torpedoes, though most weapons in this class will not enter service until the early 1990s. The principal newcomer will be the

Sikorsky SH-60B Seahawk, armed with two Honeywell Mk 46 torpedoes, about to be winched down to the aft deck of a guided missile frigate. (Sikorsky)

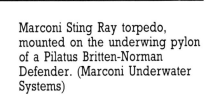

Marconi Sting Ray torpedo, mounted on the underwing pylon of a Pilatus Britten-Norman Defender. (Marconi Underwater Systems)

Honeywell Mk 50 ALWT (Advanced LightWeight Torpedo), which is to have a thermal engine, though its design is optimised for deep operation. France's contender is the electrically-driven **Murène,** which uses a special silver aluminium-oxide battery and composite construction. It will also have a dual-speed cruise, at 38 or 50 knots (70 or 93 km/hr), and an endurance of 6-12 minutes, depending on the combination of speeds used. Italy's new torpedo is the **Whitehead Moto Fides A.290,** which replaces the same company's **A.244S,** and is scheduled to enter service in 1992-93. To compete with these overseas developments, Sting Ray will be the subject of an update programme.

Few details are available of any modern lightweight torpedoes, but the **Mk 46 Mod 5** is typical in size and weight, having a length of 102 inches (2600 mm), a diameter of 12.75 inches (230 mm) and a launch weight of 512 lb (232.4 kg).

Depth Charges

In ship-launched form, depth charges were the first type of ASW weapon, being employed as early as the First World War. They are basically cylindrical weapons with a simple tail added to suit aircraft release, and a fuse that gives detonation after a pre-set time or at a pre-set depth. Some depth charges employ nuclear warheads, but these are restricted to use in deep water, to limit fall-out.

The RN employs the Mk 11 depth charge from its helicopters, for attacks on submarines and surface vessels in shallow water. This weapon has recently been modified to ensure that the fuse gives an accurate detonation depth, and is able to tolerate the severe vibration levels associated with rotary-wing aircraft operation. In addition, its nose section and outer casing have been strengthened to prevent distortion on entering the water at high speed.

The resulting **Mk 11 Mod 3** depth charge, produced by British Aerospace, is now in service with the RN and overseas navies, and is approved for use with the Navy Lynx, Sea King, Wessex and Wasp. It weighs 145 kg, of which 80 kg represents the high explosive filling. It has a length of 1397 mm and a diameter of 279 mm.

Sea Mines

The lighter types of sea mine may be laid from fixed- and rotary-wing aircraft. Mines may float, or sit on the bottom, or be moored at a pre-set height above the bottom. They can be detonated by contact, or by some form of influence fuse, eg acoustic, magnetic, pressure, or a combination of these effects.

The latest US series is the **Quickstrike** family of bottom mines, intended for use in shallow water (ie, 100 m or less). The largest is the 900 kg Mk 65, which is a completely new design, but the Mks 62, 63 and 64

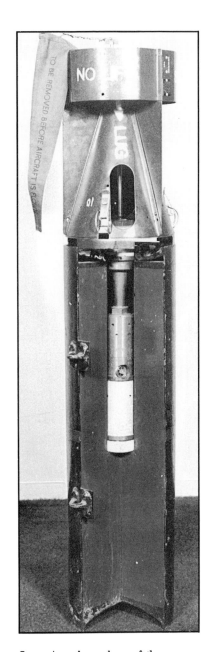

A sectioned mockup of the British Aerospace Mk 11 Mod 3 air-launched depth charge. (BAe)

A Marconi Stonefish naval ground mine being released from an RAF C-130 Hercules, serial XV218. (Marconi Underwater Systems)

are adaptations of the Mk 80 bomb series, with proportionally thicker cases.

Earlier US aircraft-laid mines included the 570 kg Mk 52 bottom mine, the 1000 kg Mk 55 bottom mine, and the 1010 kg Mk 56 moored mine. Three bottom mines—the Mk 36, Mk 40 and Mk 41—were based on the Mk 82, Mk 83 and Mk 84 bombs respectively. The Type 115A is a lightweight surface mine, weighing only 61 kg.

Britain's **Marconi Stonefish** mine is an advanced technology weapon with an onboard computing system, processing inputs from acoustic, magnetic and pressure sensors to select its target, estimate its closest point

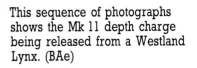

This sequence of photographs shows the Mk 11 depth charge being released from a Westland Lynx. (BAe)

of approach, and detonate the warhead.

The warstock version has a length of 2400 mm, a diameter of 530 mm, and a weight of 990 kg, including a 600 kg warhead.

Medium/Long-Range ASMs

One of the lessons learned from the US attacks on Libya in 1986 was that there is an urgent need for a precision long-range weapon that can be used against high-value targets in ports and inland. The outcome is **SLAM (Standoff Land Attack Missile),** a derivative of the AGM-84D Harpoon. In the first instance this McDonnell Douglas proposal was based on USN interest, though the USAF is expected to join the programme, which has excellent export prospects. As currently conceived, SLAM will be somewhat larger than Harpoon, weighing approximately 1385 lb (628 kg), and providing a range of more than 60 nm (110 km). The radar equipment of Harpoon will be replaced by the IIR seeker of the Maverick AGM-65D/F, and SLAM will also have a GPS receiver and the data-link from the Walleye missile. The USN plans to fire SLAM from the A-6 and F/A-18 series.

The SLAM is only an interim system, however, current USN plans calling for its replacement in the mid-1990s by **AIWS (Advanced**

Interdiction Weapons System), which will also supersede Paveway 2, Skipper 2, Walleye and the AGM-65E Laser Maverick. The AIWS is currently envisaged as a swing-wing glide weapon that will carry an HE warhead of 1000 or 2000 lb (454 or 907 kg), or a submunition-dispenser.

The **Aérospatiale ASMP** *(Air-Sol Moyenne Portée)* is a medium-range nuclear weapon that entered service with the Mirage IVP in May 1986, and will later equip the Mirage 2000N and Super Etendard. At launch it weighs approximately 1850 lb (840 kg), and it carries a 300 kT warhead over a range of up to 135 nm (250 km), the corresponding figure for a low-level launch being 43 nm (80 km). At altitude the ASMP can reach Mach 3, but at sea level its maximum is Mach 2. It is initially accelerated by a solid rocket motor that occupies the combustion chamber of a liquid-fuel ramjet.

The **Boeing AGM-131A SRAM-2** (Short-Range Attack Missile 2) was formerly known as the AASM (Advanced Air-Surface Missile), and is currently in full-scale development to replace the same company's AGM-69 SRAM, of which 1500 were delivered to equip the B-52G/H and the F-111. Primarily intended for defence suppression, the SRAM-2 will provide more range and better accuracy and a longer service life, although it is only two-thirds the size of the SRAM-1. Propulsion is to be provided by a rocket motor, and first flight is scheduled for 1989, with IOC to follow in 1992. It is anticipated that the USAF will purchase 1633 rounds for use on the B-1B and ATB.

The most important aircraft-launched weapon so far developed in the West is probably the **Boeing AGM-86B ALCM** (Air-Launched Cruise Missile), which has been operational with the B-52 since late 1982 and is scheduled to equip the B-1B. The ALCM is a swing-wing missile weighing around 3000 lb (1360 kg), powered by a 600 lb (272 kg) Williams F107-WR-100 turbofan, and providing a range of over 1350 nm (2500 km). It

The Boeing AGM-86B Air-Launched Cruise Missile (ALCM) in flight with its wings outswept. (Boeing)

Left: Test firing of an Aérospatiale ASMP supersonic missile with a nuclear warhead, from a Dassault-Breguet Mirage IV. (Aérospatiale)

has a 150kT W80-1 nuclear warhead, and navigates by a combination of inertial inputs and terrain-contour matching ie, by comparing radar altimeter data with stored information on the local terrain. The B-52 can carry eight ALCMs on an internally-mounted rotary launcher and a further 12 under the wings. In the case of the B-1B, eight can be carried internally and up to 14 under the fuselage. It is anticipated that the USAF will purchase more than 1700 ALCMs.

The replacement for the ALCM is the **General Dynamics AGM-129 ACM** (Advanced Cruise Missile), which is to feature 'stealth' technology. Very little is known of the ACM, beyond the fact that it will provide substantial improvements in range, survivability, accuracy and targeting flexibility. Reports that the USAF will have a total of around 3000 ALCMs of the two types suggest that there will be approximately 1300 ACMs.

The Soviet Union has a wide range of medium-range air-launched missiles, most of which were developed primarily to attack US carrier battle groups. During the 1980s the first of a new generation has appeared in the form of the **AS-15 Kent,** which has been operational with the Tu-95 Bear-H since 1984 and is expected to equip the new Blackjack bomber. The AS-15 is a small subsonic nuclear-tipped weapon, broadly comparable to the General Dynamics Tomahawk (which is not used in an air-launched form), and with a range of around 1600 nm (3000 km).

Chapter 5

Air - Air Guided Weapons

IN THE SAME WAY that Germany developed some basic types of ASM during the Second World War as a means to achieve a kill from outside the range of the target's defences, AAMs were developed primarily to destroy USAAF B-17s from outside the reach of the hail of 0.50-inch (12.7 mm) machine gun fire that surrounded tight formations of these bombers. There were two principal lines of development: the Henschel Hs 298 and the Ruhrstahl/BMW X-4. Both used command guidance, the former by radio and the latter using wires, but neither achieved operational status before the end of the war.

Following the advent of the Cold War in the later 1940s, the development of AAMs was restarted by both sides, in view of the vital importance of providing effective defence against nuclear bombers. Aside from being able to attack from outside the range of defensive fire (which in the Soviet case consisted of high-velocity 23 mm cannon), it soon became a question of destroying the bomber before it had time to launch a stand-off missile. Weapons thus began to be assessed in terms of their probability of putting the target out of control (eg, wing broken off, or both pilots dead) within perhaps 30 seconds of warhead detonation.

In the early postwar years so many difficulties were encountered in trying to develop satisfactory guidance systems that some experts suggested it would be better (in attacking a high altitude docile target) to use an unguided missile and compensate for its large miss distance with a powerful warhead. One result was the Douglas MB-1 Genie, which had no guidance system but a nuclear warhead.

Following the German lead, attempts were made by both sides to

produce command-guided (more specifically, beam-riding) weapons, though without any major success. Britain's **Fairey Fireflash** was supposed to introduce the RAF to this new class of weapons, but it saw only limited service on the Supermarine Swift. Fireflash was intended to fly down a modulated radar beam that was fixed relative to the longitudinal axis of the fighter, the pilot simply keeping his gunsight on the target. Unfortunately, the boost motors often failed to jettison, and the proximity fuse proved unreliable. Beam-riding also has the disadvantage that miss distance increases with firing range and with target manoeuvre. This form of guidance has merit in the context of ground-launched anti-tank missiles, but not in general for use against aircraft, which are best attacked with homing weapons. Laser beam-riding may nonetheless prove suitable for a missile to be fired by one helicopter against another, a proposed application for the Bofors RBS70.

Homing missiles make use of the energy emanating from the target either on IR or radar wavelengths. Both types of guidance have major advantages and disadvantages, hence the designer's choice is largely dictated by the operational requirements of the particular missile.

Infra-red homing is a passive system, ie, it relies entirely on the energy produced by the target, rather than depending on the target being illuminated by an external source. The IR seeker uses material that is sensitive to heat energy of a particular frequency, chosen to correspond to

These two trials installation Hawker Hunters illustrate early British developments in air-air missiles. The F4 in the foreground (XF310) carries the Blue Sky (Fairey Fireflash) with external boost motors. The aircraft nose is extended to take a modified radar ranging equipment. The F6 in the background (XF378) is equipped with Blue Jay (DH Firestreak) and AI.20 radar. (British Aerospace)

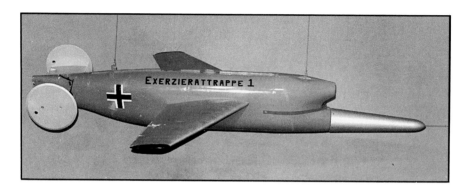

This mockup of the Henschel Hs 298V-2 air-air missile was shown at the 1975-76 'Wings of the Eagle' exhibition at the RAF Museum. (Roy Braybrook)

one of the 'windows' in the atmospheric absorption spectrum, where energy loss due to water vapour, carbon dioxide, etc is minimal. The shortest wavelength relates to the very high temperature of the turbine blades, hence such a system will function only when the seeker is looking directly up the target jetpipe. This restricts attack to a tail-chase situation, but this type of seeker (lead sulphide) has the advantage that it does not need to be cooled. A seeker chosen to suit longer wavelengths (eg, indium antimonide) can home on to the plume of hot gas behind the target before acquiring the engine, and thus makes possible all-aspect attacks, but needs cooling. A high-speed 'stealth' aircraft may need to be attacked using even longer wavelengths, the seeker detecting kinetic heating of the target's nose and leading edges.

The great advantage of IR homing is that the seeker can determine the position of the target jetpipe with great precision, hence miss distances are very small (of the order of one metre). This allows a light warhead to be used, this lightness being reflected in the weight of the complete missile. The original AIM-9 Sidewinder weighed only 165 lb (75 kg), yet it was a good weapon for its day.

The disadvantage of IR homing is that, although it is a good day/night clear weather system, it cannot see through cloud or precipitation, hence all-weather capability demands a radar missile. It is also arguable that IR missiles are relatively easily decoyed by the sun or brightly illuminated clouds, or by flares released by the target at the right time. Long endurance aircraft may also defeat IR missiles by the use of countermeasure pods, which generate pulses of IR energy that produce spurious guidance demands in most current missiles. However, these various shortcomings are being eliminated by new generations of IR missiles with imaging seekers and the ability to compute the speed of the perceived target.

Radar missiles are currently either active or semi-active, although in the longer term there will undoubtedly be passive homers, making use of the target's own radar transmissions. Active radar homing (in which the missile homes on to the reflected energy from its own transmissions) is somewhat limited in capability, due to the small power transmitted and the restriction on antenna diameter, though it is a useful alternative to IR homing as a terminal guidance phase. Semi-active radar homing provides much better range and target discrimination, since it exploits the far more powerful radar of the launch aircraft, but it has the disadvantage that the launch aircraft must continue toward the target throughout the flight of the missile, possibly exposing itself to short-range return fire.

Against the true all-weather capability of radar homing must be reckoned the disadvantage that miss distance is increased due to 'glint'. The radar missile sees the target rather like a great wobbling jelly covered in sequins. As it gets closer, the apparent centre of the target moves around the airframe (according to the precise direction from which it is viewed), hence the miss distance is far greater than for an IR missile that sees only one small fixed source of energy. Radar missiles are consequently heavier, since they need a larger warhead. In addition, as semi-active homing provides target acquisition at longer range than IR, such weapons have a larger rocket motor to exploit this range potential. Radar missiles may be defeated by chaff or jamming, though decoys can be identified by Doppler effect, and modern weapons are much more resistant to ECM.

Before leaving this general introduction to the technology of AAMs, it is relevant to outline the principles used in the guidance equations and the types of warhead currently in use.

Homing missiles traditionally use **proportional navigation,** although this basic idea is often modified to suit the individual weapon. The homing head is maintained pointing directly at the target, and rate gyros attached to the gimbals on which the seeker is mounted measure the variation in the relative target position, ie, the sightline spin rate. Virtually all missiles are of cruciform layout (rather than using "roll and pull" like an aeroplane), and the control surfaces are rotated to provide g-loadings in the two corresponding planes that are proportional to the sightline spin components. In essence, the guidance system works to reduce the sightline spin rate to zero, hence proportional navigation boils down to the old mariner's rule that, if another ship is on a constant bearing, there is going to be a collision (or the two ships are on parallel headings at the same speed).

The AIM-7 Sparrow illustrates one variation of proportional navigation, in which the navigation ratio (ie, the ratio of missile turn rate to sightline spin rate) is made proportional to closing velocity, as measured by Doppler effect. In addition, since the launch aircraft should ideally be heading toward the computed missile impact point when the weapon is released, any error in this heading is corrected immediately after launch by a command known as 'English bias', which turns the weapon in the right direction before it locks on to the target.

The warhead is normally detonated by a contact or proximity fuse (with a delay of a few milliseconds to place the missile inside the structure or alongside the engines or cockpit), although it could be done by the guidance head, as the sightline spin rate goes off the scale. A **contact fuse** may take the form of a frangible wire in the wing leading edges, or a piezo-electric crystal that is crushed by an inertia load. **Proximity fuses** have generally been based on Doppler radar effect or IR (which can give a precise indication of passing the target jetpipe nozzle), but the use of lasers appears to be gaining in popularity.

Blast warheads naturally have the highest percentage of explosive, but the intensity of the resulting pressure wave falls off very quickly as miss distance increases, hence they are probably best suited to missiles that are intended to hit to kill ('hittiles'). **Fragmentation** warheads usually consist of an explosive charge surrounded by a cylinder of steel that is grooved like a chocolate bar, although in at least one recent design this metallic casing is replaced by pre-cut tungsten fragments embedded in a plastic casting. Fragmenting warheads are better suited to large miss distances (since fragment density falls off with the square of radius, whereas blast intensity varies with the cube of radius), but the scattering of the fragments arguably reduces their potential for structural damage.

In the 1950s the idea was advanced that the energy of the warhead explosion could best be employed in the creation of an expanding ring of metal. Ideally, this would give a continuous cut across the fuselage or wing of the target (rather than a series of scattered holes), and it might even be that some of the energy associated with fragments missing the target would be passed through this ring into the structure. The concept was simple enough; the problem was to manufacture a warhead that would produce this **continuous rod**. In the end a close approximation to the desired result was achieved by welding together a series of rods. Under the force of the explosion the welds become plastic and then break, but constrain the movement of the rods long enough to form them into an expanding circle. The result is a linear series of slashes in the skin of the target, significantly reducing its strength, although damage to aircraft systems may be less than for a simple fragmentation warhead.

Short-Range AAMs

The outstanding short-range AAM of the first postwar generation (and perhaps the second) was the **AIM-9 Sidewinder,** which was originally developed by the US Navy facility at China Lake, California, a station now known as the Naval Weapons Center. It is true that the **Hughes AIM-4 Falcon** (which also entered service in 1956 and was also designed in IR and radar versions) was even smaller, being intended for internal carriage on the F-102. The AIM-4 initially weighed only 110 lb (50 kg)! It is also true that Britain's **DH Firestreak** was superior to the AIM-9 in certain respects, notably in its ability to discriminate between actual targets and brightly-lit clouds. What made the AIM-9 stand out was its combination of simplicity, ingenuity, reliability, performance, development potential, and (ultimately) its war record.

Unlike Firestreak, the AIM-9 did not have to be stored in a controlled environment, nor did it require preflight checks. It could be handled virtually like a round of ammunition: provided it would actually fit on the

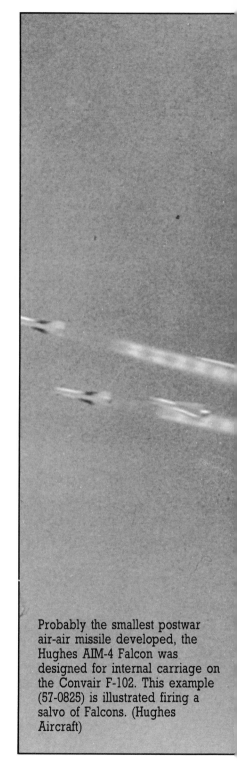

Probably the smallest postwar air-air missile developed, the Hughes AIM-4 Falcon was designed for internal carriage on the Convair F-102. This example (57-0825) is illustrated firing a salvo of Falcons. (Hughes Aircraft)

This kinetheodolite picture shows a de Havilland Firestreak being fired from an RAAF Sabre at a height of 40,000 ft over the Woomera range in Southern Australia against a Jindivik target. (British Aerospace)

launch rail, it was ready to fire. Whereas conventional missiles had their roll rates limited by a rate gyro and a roll control circuit, the AIM-9 was given patented 'Rollerons', slipstream-driven turbines in free-floating ailerons, the turbines acting as gyros to cancel any roll by precession.

Likewise, whereas any normal missile continuously compares the G demanded by the homing head and the actual lateral G, and changes the tail angle accordingly, the AIM-9 simply made the pressure supplied to the control surface actuator proportional to the G-demand (with no feedback of actual G). In essence, it seems that an IR seeker locates its target so precisely that all kinds of simplifications can be made to the guidance and control system without any catastrophic effect on miss distance.

Trials with the missile that became Sidewinder began in 1952, although the first success did not come until 11 September 1953, when a massive QB-17 was shot down by one launched from a Skyraider. Sidewinder entered service in 1956 and in September 1958 was first used operationally, when F-86s from Taiwan began to destroy Chinese MiG-15s and -17s, killing 27 without loss over a six week period. Unfortunately, one Sidewinder lodged in the rear fuselage of a MiG-17, its proximity and contact fuses having failed, which resulted in both the Russians and Chinese copying the missile, using their own rocket motors. In Vietnam the AIM-9 performed better than the AIM-7, though both left room for improvement, especially in the early years. In the period 1965-68 the AIM-9 is reported to have had a kill-rate of only 20 per cent, though the later AIM-9G with continuous rod warhead and improved angular acquisition limits (SEAM = Sidewinder Expanded Acquisition Mode) is credited by some sources with a kill rate of almost 50 per cent.

The best-known of current Sidewinders is the AIM-9L, which is the all-aspect variant that introduced double-delta canards. It has been used by the Israelis from F-16s on many occasions, was employed by the US Navy from F-14s to down two Su-22s in 1981, and was issued to RN Sea Harriers at the start of the Falklands Conflict of 1982. In this last case the AIM-9L was credited with 16 definite Argentine kills and one probable. Sidewinder exports outside the most favoured nations (NATO, Israel, Australia, etc) have in recent years taken the form of the less capable AIM-9P, which is a remanufactured AIM-9B/9E/9J, and the AIM-9Q.

Although the US Government is committed to not fund the development of a missile to compete with Europe's ASRAAM (described later), just as the principal European governments are committed to not produce a competitor for AMRAAM, some development of the Sidewinder series nonetheless continues. The AIM-9L is now being superseded in US production by the AIM-9M, with improved guidance, reduced-smoke motor, better target discrimination, improved counter-measures re-

Photographed during the 1982 Falklands conflict, this RN Sea Harrier is armed with two AIM-9L Sidewinders and two 30 mm Aden cannon. This particular aircraft (serial ZA177, side number 77) was the one in which Flt Lt 'Dave' Morgan made his kills. (Crown Copyright, *HMS Heron*)

136

sistance, and enhanced reliability and maintainability.

The latest Sidewinder development is the AIM-9R, formerly known as the AIM-9M Product Improvement Program (PIP). Virtually all important Sidewinder models have used IR-homing, but this is the first with an imaging seeker, which makes it far less susceptible to decoys. It reportedly also permits removal of the cryogenic cooling bottle needed for earlier all-aspect variants. The AIM-9R is to enter service in 1992, and the US Navy is expected to have around 5000 earlier models modified to this standard.

The Soviet derivative of the AIM-9B was the **AA-2 Atoll,** which superseded the beam-riding AA-1 Alkali. More recent examples of Russian short-range AAMs are the AA-8 Aphid and the AA-11 Archer, the latter being introduced with the MiG-29 and Su-27. China's PL-2 corresponds broadly to the AIM-9B and AA-2, while the PL-2A is an improved model with a more sensitive (cooled) IR seeker, equivalent to the AIM-9E.

The present export version is the **PL-5B,** which is sold through CATIC, the China National Aero-Technology Import/Export Corporation. The PL-5B reaches a maximum speed of Mach 4.5, can produce a lateral 30g, and has a firing range of up to 8.65 nm (16 km). It has compressed air cooling, and is available either with an IR proximity fuse and fragmentation

As exemplified by this aircraft (XV254) some Nimrod MR2Ps (the 'P' indicating a flight refuelling probe) were modified in 1982 to carry four Sidewinders on their Martel pylons, following three encounters over the South Atlantic with an Argentine 707-320B used for maritime reconnaissance. (British Aerospace)

warhead or a radar proximity fuse and continuous-rod warhead. The brochure refers to an accuracy of 9 metres, a lethal radius of 10 metres, and a dead zone around the sun of 16 degrees. There have also been press reports of a PL-7 with an indium antimonide seeker cooled by liquid nitrogen, and giving all-aspect attack capability, though this is evidently not yet ready for export.

Israel's developments in the AAM field began iwth the **Rafael Shafrir** 1 and 2, which have now been replaced by the same organisation's **Python 3.** Described by Rafael as a third generation AAM with all-aspect capabilities similar to those of the AIM-9L, the Python 3 is much heavier than Sidewinder, although its maximum launch range is only 8 nm (15 km). The weight difference may be explained by the fact that the Israeli weapon

The Rafael Shafrir short-range missile, photographed on an IAI Kfir-C2 at Le Bourget in 1977. (Roy Braybrook)

The Rafael Python 3, likewise on a Kfir. Note the massive slipstream-driven 'Rollerons', which automatically restrict roll rate. (Rafael)

has a very powerful motor, to deal with load factors up to 56 g at sea level. Its warhead of tungsten fragments is also very heavy, to produce lethal results at a miss distance of 23 ft (7 m). A Doppler radar proximity fuse is used, but this is linked to the IR seeker for resistance to countermeasures. Python 3 was delivered to the Israeli Air Force in 1981 and was used operationally during the invasion of Lebanon in 1982. It is claimed to have killed 'tens of aircraft' without one failure.

France's short-range AAM is the **Matra 550 Magic** series, characterised by its twin canard surfaces, the front set fixed and the

The Matra 550 Magic on the tip rail of a Mirage F1 from the French Air Force's 12th Fighter Wing (EC.12). The aircraft also has a Matra Super 530F on its underwing pylon. (Matra)

Test-firing of a Magic 2 dogfight missile from a Mirage 2000 of EC.1/2 *'Cigognes'*, the first unit to receive these aircraft. (CEV Cazaux)

second set acting as control surfaces. As in the case of Sidewinder, the wings are at the rear and fixed. The object of the double canard arrangement is presumably to prevent the controls stalling at high angles of attack (AOA), the missile being designed for 50g. Magic 1 entered service in 1976, and over 7000 rounds were built for 14 countries. It has been used successfully by Iraq in the Gulf War with Iran. Magic 2 is an all-aspect derivative, now operational on French Air Force Mirage 2000s. It is claimed to have the first mass-produced multi-element cell IR homing head, allowing it to discriminate against decoy flares and IR jammers. The seeker is cooled with gaseous nitrogen from a bottle in the launcher.

South Africa's **Armscor Kukri** might be mistaken for Magic at a glance, but in fact it is a lighter, smaller missile with less range and a completely different control system. The Kukri is the export version of the **V3B,** which is operational with the South African Air Force on the Mirage III and F1 series. Instead of generating lateral accelerations on two perpendicular axes (as the vast majority of cruciform missiles do), this weapon has a roll-and-steer guidance system and thus flies more like an aircraft. It is also unusual in having a look-and-launch sighting system, the missile seeker being slaved to the pilot's helmet. Within 20 degrees of the aircraft longitudinal axis, the seeker follows the movement of the pilot's head, and a small unit on his helmet projects a sighting reticle on the visor. On sighting a target, the pilot places the reticle on it, and hears a growl to indicate that the seeker has acquired its IR signal. He can then switch to a tracking mode (which releases the missile from following his helmet motion), and, if he so decides, fire the weapon. The Kukri may also be used in a caged mode, in which the seeker is locked to aircraft axis, and the pilot aims with the gunsight.

Because of its bank-and-pull guidance, only the pitch controls need to be protected with flow-straighteners at high AOA, the roll canards operating in isolation. The tail fins are free to rotate about the body of the missile, and thus produce stability in pitch and yaw without generating damping in roll. This concept is very ingenious, but lateral acceleration is limited to 35g, and it may be that the Kukri has a larger miss distance than Magic 2. Nonetheless, with a warhead effective to a distance of 30 ft (9 m), the Kukri is clearly a lethal weapon, with considerable development potential.

Several other short-range AAMs exist, although detailed descriptions are not available. Brazil's **MAA-1 Piranha** has been developed by the Instituto de Atividades Espaciais, is broadly similar to the AIM-9 in configuration, and may possibly be in production. Taiwan's **Sky Sword 1** is also similar to Sidewinder, and is being developed by the Chung San Institute of Science and Technology. Reports indicate that it has been test fired as far back as May 1986, but its exact status has not been published.

The missile that is expected to replace Sidewinder in most NATO air forces is the **AIM-132 ASRAAM** (Advanced Short-Range Air-Air Missile), which is currently at the project definition phase, being studied by British Aerospace, Norway's Raufoss, and Germany's Bodenseewerk. Together with the medium-range AMRAAM, ASRAAM is the subject of a'

Mock-up of the AIM-132 ASRAAM with launch-rail and an adaptor, mounted below the outboard pylon of an RN Sea Harrier. The clenched-fist badge denotes No 899 Sqn, the Headquarters Squadron at RNAS Yeovilton. (British Aerospace)

Memorandum of Understanding (MoU) signed by the defence ministers of the US, UK, France and Germany in August 1980. The object of the MoU was to reduce duplication of R&D, the Sidewinder replacement being developed only in Europe, and the Sparrow replacement only in the US. France has opted out of ASRAAM development, but could join either programme at a later stage.

Very little is known of ASRAAM, beyond the fact that, in comparison with the AIM-9, it will have better off-boresight capability, a higher speed, a better hit probability and a higher terminal lethality. It will also have a much larger firing volume around the target, especially in the forward hemisphere. Reports suggest that ASRAAM will be linked to a helmet-mounted sight, and may use two-stage guidance, eg, inertial navigation with IR terminal homing. Its configuration is unusual in that it has no wings, but four control fins at the rear. The prime contractor for ASRAAM is BBG, a company that combines the initials of BAe and Bodenseewerk Geraetetechnik. Raufoss is a subcontractor to BBG. The new weapon is expected to enter service in the mid-1990s.

Before leaving the subject of short-range AAMs, it may be noted that such weapons are now being applied to helicopters. This new development appears to be inspired by belief that the Soviet Mi-24 Hind has an air-air role, and that NATO helicopters might also need to defend themselves against the Su-25 Frogfoot. The natural weapon choice for a rotary-wing aircraft is perhaps a lightweight SAM, since such missiles are designed to be fired from launchers which have no forward speed, but some lightweight AAMs are also proving suitable.

The first Western helicopter to receive AAMs as a standard fit is probably the US Marine Corps AH-1W Super Cobra, which is being given provisions for two **AIM-9Ls** in addition to its 20 mm three-barrel M197 cannon. The US Army has been conducting trials of helicopter air-air combat (HAAC), and now plans to equip 730 Bell OH-58C/Ds with the

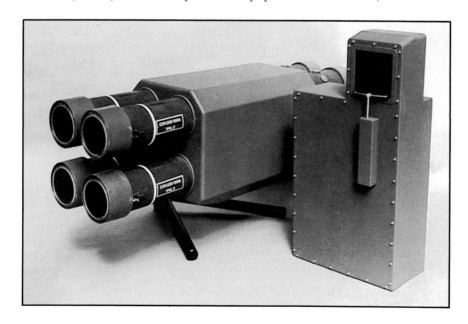

Mock-up of the RBS70 missile system configured for use on a helicopter, with four-round launcher pod and sight/control unit. (Bofors)

General Dynamics Stinger. This is also planned as armament for the US Army's UH-60 Black Hawk and some AH-1 Cobras. The air-to-air Stinger (ATAS) has the advantage of being an extremely light weapon: a loaded two-round launcher weighs a mere 123 lb (56 kg). Like the AIM-9, Stinger is an IR-homer, and is thus a fire-and-forget missile, but the latter has the further advantage of being a 'hittile' and thus avoids proximity fuse ECM problems.

France has a suitable basis for a helicopter missile in the form of the **Matra Mistral** lightweight SAM (another IR homer), which is proposed as the **AATCP** *(air-air très courte portée)* for the Gazelle and Dauphin, and later the Eurocopter CATH. Another such development is that proposed for Sweden's **Bofors RBS70,** which differs in being a laser beam rider. It has a range of up to 5000 metres, and offers complete immunity from jamming.

Medium/Long-Range AAMs

Although ASRAAM represents a major programme for Europe, especially if it is accepted by the US services, it has to be borne in mind that (despite the continuing use of short-range dogfights in every conflict to date) there is a swing in defence philosophy that emphasises the importance of medium/long range weapons.

It may well be that Vietnam was misleading, since the rules of engagement placed severe restraints on the use of the **AIM-7 Sparrow** with semi-active radar homing. In general, US fighter pilots were required to identify the target visually, hence the only way to use the medium-range AIM-7 was to have another aircraft approach the target, or alternatively to close with the target, identify it, and fall back before firing. This restriction was based on the well-known unreliability of IFF equipment, and on the fact that the vast majority of aircraft in the area were American. This vis-ident requirement was relaxed to some extent in the 1972 bombing campaign, and it is believed that the Israelis had no such requirement in the 1973 war. In any event, the effect of a vis-ident demand is to de-emphasise BVR (beyond-visual-range) weapons in favour of guns and short-range AAMs. In the Falklands conflict of 1982, the RN Sea Harriers had only guns and Sidewinders, hence the only aerial combats were dogfights.

Another reason why BVR missiles played no great part in the Vietnam War was that the AIM-7 proved disappointing. The main Sparrow variant was the AIM-7E, which had entered production in 1963. It had a 66 lb (30 kg) continuous rod warhead and a maximum head-on range of 14 nm (26 km). The AIM-7 was felt to have poor reliability due mainly to its ancient avionics (deliveries of the Sparrow III began in 1958). It was also criticised for its excessive minimum launch range, the long delay between lock-on and firing, and its poor results against manoeuvring targets. According to published reports, the average AIM-7 kill-rate between 1965 and 1968 was a mere 9 per cent! In 1969 deliveries began of the AIM-7E-2,

with improved manoeuvrability and reduced minimum launch range. The AIM-7F was a major step forwards, with miniaturised avionics, a 90 lb (41 kg) warhead, and a range of up to 24 nm (44 km), but it arrived only in 1975, too late to take part in the conflict.

The poor showing of the AIM-7E, combined with the vis-ident problem, tended to support the widely-held belief that any shooting war invariably comes down to visual contact and short-range weapons. It is clear, however, that the development of reliable IFF equipment and outstanding BVR missiles would change the balance of importance in favour of longer range weapons.

The other factor behind the current swing in favour of BVR weapons is the growing realisation that NATO fighters are badly outnumbered by their Warsaw Pact counterparts, hence Western technology must be used to produce a kill-ratio in a one-vs-many situation. The only way to achieve

The semi-recessed carriage of the AIM-7 Sparrow series is illustrated by this underside view of an RAF F-4 carrying a BAe Sky Flash, which has the same external shape as the AIM-7E. (British Aerospace)

144

this objective is detect and destroy the enemy at longer ranges than he can achieve, and to use short-range weapons only to finish off the few survivors.

The NATO fighter will thus detect his targets at long range, accelerate to provide the maximum possible firing range, release four AMRAAMs at four targets, and then make a maximum rate turn to minimise the risk from return fire. In the ideal case, all of the enemy aircraft will have been destroyed without visual contact. Only if an enemy aircraft has survived the opening salvo will ASRAAM and cannon be brought into use, hence for this type of engagement these types of armament are of secondary importance. For NATO air forces to win in a one-vs-many scenario, AMRAAM is the crucial factor.

In considering the principal medium-range AAMs currently in service, it is convenient to begin with the **AIM-7 Sparrow III,** since several other weapons were derived from it. The present AIM-7M is manufactured both by Raytheon and General Dynamics (Pomona Div). It features an inverse monopulse seeker that gives better lookdown performance in clutter and increases resistance to jamming. The AIM-7M also has a digital signal processor, a new autopilot, and a new fuse.

Firing of an AIM-7 from a Marine Corps F/A-18 Hornet of VFMA-323 ('The Death Rattlers'), based at MCAS El Toro. (McDonnell Douglas)

Italy's equivalent of the AIM-7M is the **Selenia Aspide.** This missile resembles Sparrow, but is apparently a completely different weapon, developed specifically for the F-104S Starfighter. At the 1987 Paris Air Show, Selenia unveiled the **Idra** AAM, derived from the Aspide, but using multi-stage guidance. Full details were not revealed, but the inertial phase is evidently based on a strapdown laser gyro system, and the terminal phase appears to be active J-Band pulse-Doppler radar. With a launch weight of 463 lb (210 kg), Idra will be somewhat lighter than current Sparrows. It has an active pulse-Doppler radar proximity fuse, and a warhead that throws tungsten cubes.

The basis for the Selenia proposal is that Italy, which is not a party to the four-nation MoU on ASRAAM and AMRAAM, is free to develop its own medium-range AAM as an alternative to AMRAAM for the Italian Air Force EFA. At the 1987 unveiling it was stated that the company had been working on the project for three years, and was hoping for government support in the following year, leading to firings in 1991 and initial operational capability (IOC) in 1995/96.

Britain's EFA and the Tornado F3 will use AMRAAM, but for the present the Tornado F2 and F3 are armed with the **BAe Sky Flash,** which is also used (as the Rb71) on Sweden's JA 37 Viggen. This British missile uses the air frame and warhead of the AIM-7E, but it has a Marconi monopulse radar seeker, and a British autopilot, radar proximity fuse, and electrical power unit.

Left: Air defence variants of the Tornado carry their Sky Flash missiles in slightly staggered tandem pairs, supplemented by Sidewinders on the sides of the tank pylons. (British Aerospace)

Sweden's JA 37 air defence Viggen is armed with two Sky Flashes on the inboard wing pylons, two Sidewinders outboard, and a centreline 30 mm Oerlikon KCA cannon. The '13' on the nose indicates that the aircraft is based at Norrköping with F13 wing. (A. Anderson, Saab-Scania)

In order to overcome the limitations of semi-active homing, viz, the need for continued target illumination, and inability to deal with multi-target engagements, BAe have proposed an **Active Sky Flash** that would be a fire-and-forget missile, capable of defeating multiple targets in a salvo firing. Sweden may participate in this development (under the local designation **Rb71A**) for the JAS 39. There is also some Swedish interest in a ramjet-powered derivative (**Rb73**) with an engine developed by Volvo Flygmotor with either Marquardt or Aérospatiale.

France's current medium-range AAM is the **Matra Super 530D** for the Mirage 2000. This weapon is basically a derivative of the Matra R.530 used on the Mirage III series, the intermediate step being the Super 530F for the Mirage F1. The 'Super D' uses semi-active radar homing (like its predecessors), but in this case the homing head is designed for use with a Doppler radar, fully digitised, and protected against ECM. It is somewhat heavier than the Sparrow family, primarily because of its powerful rocket motor, which gives a snap-up/down capability of 40,000 ft (12,000 m) and a maximum speed of almost Mach 5. In order to deal with the high structural temperatures associated with such high speeds, the Super D has a stainless steel fuselage and a silica radome. Service acceptance trials at the Cazaux

147

The first generation of French medium-range AAMs was represented by the Matra R.530, which is shown here on the underwing pylons of a Mirage F1, the weapons on the tips being the short-range Matra Magic. This particular F1 (c/n 211) is coded 5-NH, and is flown by EC.1/5 *'Vendée',* based at Orange. (Dassault-Breguet)

Firing of the Matra Super 530D from the third prototype Mirage 2000. (CEV Cazaux)

Centre d'Essais en Vol (Flight Test Centre) established a firing range of more than 21.5 nm (40 km), and the missile is now in production.

The missile to succeed the Super 530D is the **Matra MICA** *(Missile d'Interception et de Combat Aérien),* which will also replace the Magic 2 short-range AAM. The idea behind this concept is that advances in miniaturisation now allow a relatively small missile, weighing only 243 lb (110 kg), to use multi-stage guidance and have a firing range of up to 27 nm (50 km). The MICA will have interchangeable radar and IR homing heads, and jet-deflector controls. For short-range firings the homing head will be used for single-stage guidance, but for longer ranges mid-course inertial

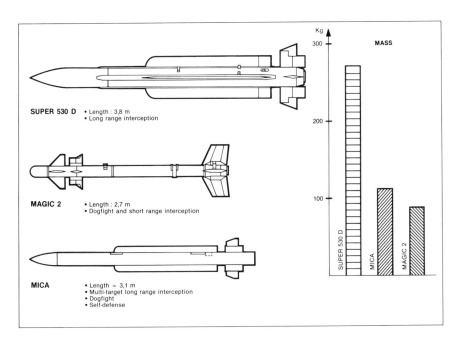

The Matra family of air-air missiles, illustrating the remarkably small size and
weight of MICA in comparison with the Super 530D. (Matra)

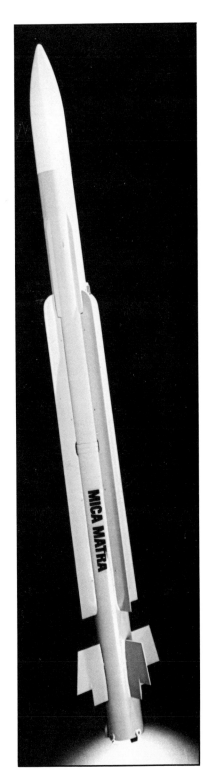

guidance is available, with provisions for target updating by the launch
aircraft during the flight of the missile. The MICA will arm both the Mirage
2000 and the Rafale series.

The **Hughes/Raytheon AIM-120 AMRAAM** is undoubtedly the most
important air-air weapon for most next generation Allied fighters.
Compared with Sparrow, it is somewhat lighter at 327 lb (148 kg), and it is
controlled by its tailfins, whereas the AIM-7 has fixed tailfins and moving
wings. In addition, AMRAAM has active radar terminal homing, giving
multi-target engagements, and a home-on-jam facility. It will replace the
AIM-7 on all USAF and USN fighters, although the 270 F-16A air defence
fighters that are replacing F-4s and F-106s with 11 Air National Guard units
will retain the AIM-7. The AMRAAM will also equip RAF Tornado F3s, RN
Sea Harriers, and German Air Force F-4Fs. Current plans call for 24,335
rounds for the US services alone, with an average price ceiling of $259,000
in Fy84 values, and IOC in 1989.

The new generation Soviet medium-range AAM is the **AA-10 Alamo,**
which has been seen on the MiG-29 and Su-27. The basic configuration of
this weapon is unusual, in that it has three sets of lifting surfaces, the central
group having reverse taper. The AA-10 is thought to exist in at least three
versions: a dogfight missile with a hemispherical IR homing head and a

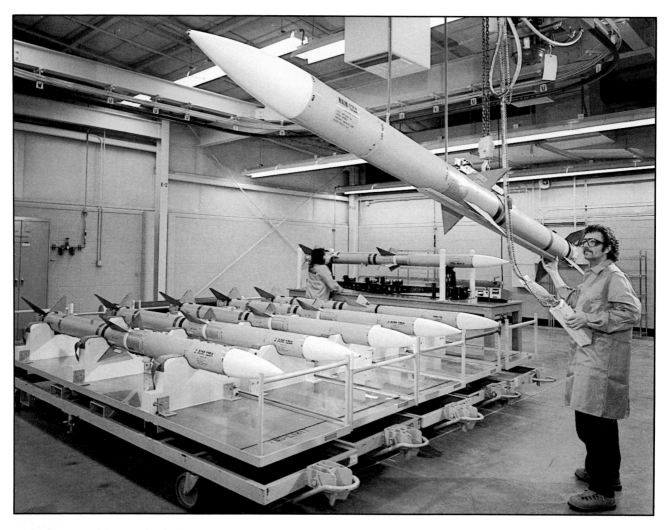

The preparation of AIM-120 AMRAAMs for delivery, at the Hughes Aircraft plant at Tucson, Arizona. (Hughes)

The first photograph released of an AMRAAM firing from an F/A-18. This aircraft (serial 161705), attached to the Pacific Missile Test Center at Point Mugu, California, fired two missiles, the first destroying the target and the second passing through the debris. (Hughes Aircraft)

short rocket motor, and two longer-range radar versions with ogival heads. It has been suggested that one of these has active homing, while the other may have some form of passive radar homing. If this is the case, then the Soviet have clearly stolen a lead over the West.

In the long-range AAM category, the principal Soviet weapons are the **AA-6 Acrid** of the MiG-25 and the **AA-9 Amos** of the MiG-31, the latter possibly being equivalent to the **Hughes AIM-54 Phoenix** of the F-14 Tomcat.

A Phoenix-armed F-14A, about to be launched from the deck of a US Navy carrier. Note the massive ventral fairings to accommodate the fuselage-mounted missiles, and the empty Sidewinder rail cantilevered off the Phoenix wing pylon. (Hughes Aircraft)

Firing of Phoenix from an F-14A (serial 160679) of the Miramar NAS-based VF-51. The 'NL' tail-code currently refers to the CVN-70 *Carl Vinson*. (Hughes Aircraft)

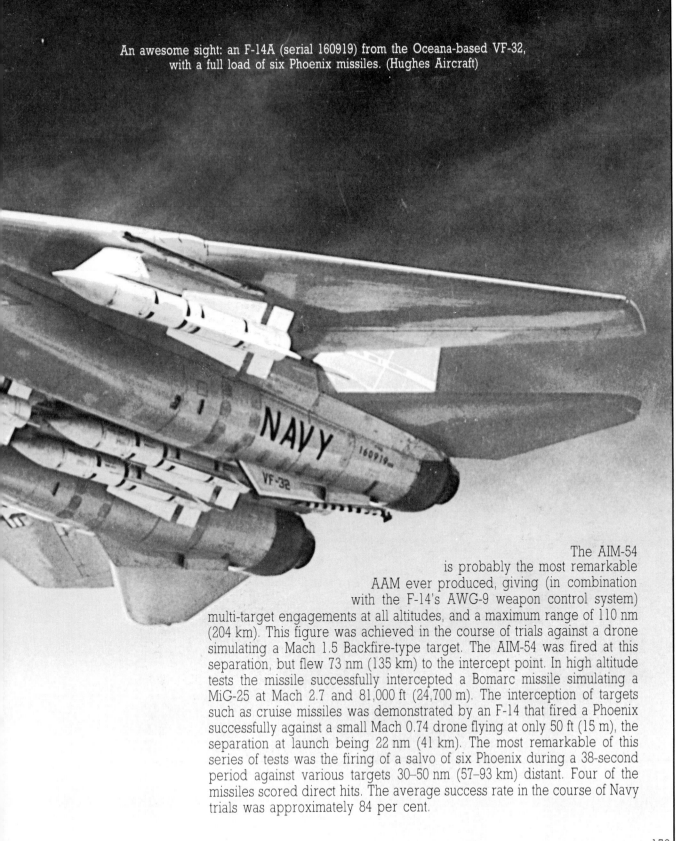

An awesome sight: an F-14A (serial 160919) from the Oceana-based VF-32, with a full load of six Phoenix missiles. (Hughes Aircraft)

The AIM-54 is probably the most remarkable AAM ever produced, giving (in combination with the F-14's AWG-9 weapon control system) multi-target engagements at all altitudes, and a maximum range of 110 nm (204 km). This figure was achieved in the course of trials against a drone simulating a Mach 1.5 Backfire-type target. The AIM-54 was fired at this separation, but flew 73 nm (135 km) to the intercept point. In high altitude tests the missile successfully intercepted a Bomarc missile simulating a MiG-25 at Mach 2.7 and 81,000 ft (24,700 m). The interception of targets such as cruise missiles was demonstrated by an F-14 that fired a Phoenix successfully against a small Mach 0.74 drone flying at only 50 ft (15 m), the separation at launch being 22 nm (41 km). The most remarkable of this series of tests was the firing of a salvo of six Phoenix during a 38-second period against various targets 30–50 nm (57–93 km) distant. Four of the missiles scored direct hits. The average success rate in the course of Navy trials was approximately 84 per cent.

The original Phoenix supplied to the US Navy and Iran (the only F-14 operators) was the AIM-54A. This was duly superseded by the -54B and -54C, the latter having a Northrop strapdown inertial navigation system and a new proximity fuse. The current model is the **AIM-54C +**, which is reported to have improved capability against manoeuvring aircraft and low-flying cruise missiles, especially in a jamming environment. It also differs in requiring no coolant supplies from the parent aircraft.

The planned replacement for the AIM-54 is the US Navy's **AAAM (Advanced Air-Air Missile),** which is required to have more range yet be significantly lighter, so that an F-14D will be able to land with eight rounds. At present the aircraft can land with only four Phoenix. It is anticipated that this new weapon will be used not only on the F-14D, but also the US Navy's F/A-18C/D, the A-6F, and later the ATA. In addition, the AAAM will arm the F-15C/E and ATF (F-22 or -23). At present, teams combining Hughes with Raytheon and General Dynamics with Westinghouse are competing for the demonstration and validation phase, the former team proposing ramjet propulsion and combined radar/IR guidance, while the latter team prefers a solid rocket motor and semi-active radar. A production run of up to 4000 rounds is planned, with deliveries beginning in the late 1990s.

From time to time there are references to passive radar homing

Future long-range air-air missiles will probably rely on a combination of rocket and ramjet propulsion, as researched with this integral rocket-ramjet test vehicle from Vought, mounted here on an A-7. (Vought)

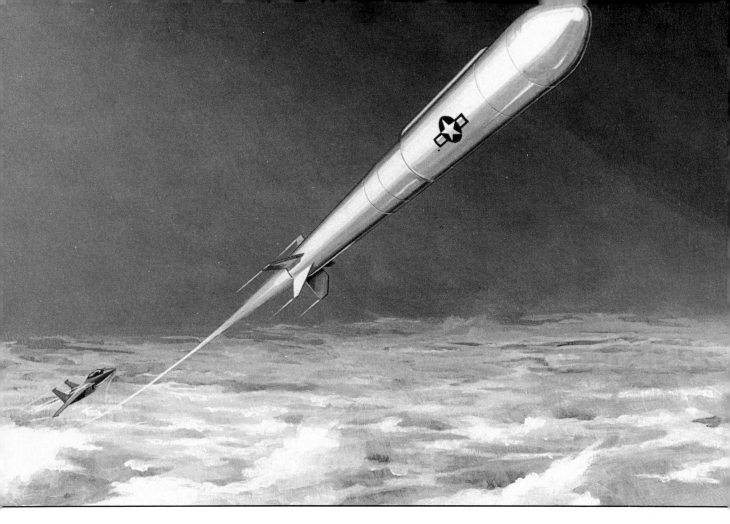

An artist's impression of the
launching of the Vought ASAT
(Anti-Satellite) two-stage weapon
from a USAF F-15. (Vought)

missiles being developed in the West, such as the proposed XAIM-97
Seekbat for use against the high-flying MiG-25/31. Another proposal is
concerned with a joint NATO development to produce an anti-radar AAM
for use against the SUAWACS aircraft. However, little hard information is
available on these projects.

Although not strictly an air-air weapon, the **ASAT** (anti-satellite)
F-15-launched missile warrants mention as an indication of the high-altitude
intercept potential of an aircraft-launched missile. The ASAT is sometimes
referred to as the miniature homing vehicle (MHV), the air-launched
miniature vehicle (ALMV), or the miniature air-launched system (MALS).
Whatever its designation, it combines a SRAM booster as the first-stage
motor and an Altair III rocket for the second stage, which has terminal IR
guidance. The ASAT is 17 ft (5.2 m) long and weighs 2700 lb (1225 kg).
Flight trials began in January 1983. It is believed to be capable of
intercepting satellites at a height of 300 nm (550 km) above the earth,
although there are plans to increase this figure to 1500 nm (2800 km). The
USAF has also proposed the establishment of two ASAT squadrons with a
total of 28 F-15s and 56 missiles, to be based at Langley AFB, Virginia and
McCord AFB Washington, but this plan has been halted by funding
restrictions.

Appendices

Armament Specifications

The following tables are provided to allow direct comparison of the most significant representatives of each weapons group. They do not constitute an exhaustive 'shopping list'.

Group 1 Automatic Weapons

Bore (mm)	Designation	Barrels (No)	Cyclic Rate (rd/min)	Muzzle Vel (m/sec)	Gun Wt (kg)
Linear-action machine guns					
5.56	FN Minimi	1	750/1100	895	5.3
7.62	FN MAG 58	1	600–1000	855	11.0
12.7	Browning M3P	1	up to 1100	900	35.0
Linear-action cannon					
20	Oerlikon KAD	1	850–1000	1040	68.0
20	GIAT M621	1	300/740	1000	58.0
25	Oerlikon KBA	1	570–600	1100	112.0
MDC Chain Guns					
7.62	MDC EX-34	1	520	862	13.7
30	MDC M230	1	625–900	N/A	55.8
Revolver cannon (older types)					
20	M39	1	1200	1000	90.0
30	Aden	1	1200–1400	790	87.0
30	DEFA 553	1	1300	820	100.0

Revolver cannon (modern designs)					
25	Aden-25	1	1650–1850	1050	92.0
27	Mauser BK27	1	1000/1700	1025	125.0
30	DEFA 554	1	1100/1800	820	100.0
30	Oerlikon KCA	1	1350	1030	136.0
30	GIAT Type 791B	1	1500/2500	1025	110.0
Twin-barrel cannon					
20	Hughes Mk 11	2	700/4200	N/A	108.8
23	GSh-23	2	3500	890	76.0
25	GE-225 Lightweight	2	750/2000	1280	86.0
GE Gatling-type machine guns					
7.62	GAU-2B/A	6	500–6000	838	18.8
12.7	GECAL-50	3	2000–4000	N/A	30.0
12.7	GECAL-50	6	up to 8000	N/A	43.5
GE Gatling-type cannon					
20	M61A1	6	6000	1030	114.0
20	Lightweight M61	6	6000	1050	93.0
25	GAU-12/U	5	3600	1097	122.0
30	GAU-8/A	7	1800–4200	1036	281.2
30	GAU-13/A	4	up to 2000	792	151.0

Group 2a Rocket Projectiles

Designation	Calibre (mm)	Length (mm)	Launch Wt (kg)	Warhead
Brandt (SNEB)	68	847–924	4.29–6.26	–
M68-ABL	68	1380	8.20	8x190 gm darts
M68-AMV	68	1380	8.30	36x35 gm darts
SNORA	81	1440–1800	12.2–18.7	4.5–11.0 kg
Type 1	90	1212	17.1	7.88 kg
Brandt	100	2510	37–42.6	14–18 kg
100MP-ABL	100	2740	39.7	36x190 gm darts
100MP-AMV	100	2740	39.7	192x35 gm darts
Bofors	135	N/A	45/46	20/21 kg (AP-frag/GP)

Note: *There is some variation in projectile weight according to the type of warhead fitted. For example, the warheads of the 81 mm SNORA vary from 4.5 to 11.0 kg, while those of the 100 mm Hotchkiss-Brandt range from 10.5 kg with eight 850 gm darts to an 18 kg demolition version for use against ships and buildings.*

Group 2b Rocket Pods

Designation	Rockets (no)	Calibre (mm)	Length (mm)	Diameter (mm)	Weight (kg)
Matra Type F2	6	68	1450	246	58
Matra Type 155	18	68	2340	410	185
Matra Type F1	36	68	2128	width 564 height 637	270
TBA 68.12L	12 multidart	68	1400	width 310 height 260	130
TBA 68.22L	22 multidart	68	1400	width 450 height 350	235
LAU 5003 A/A	19	70	1250*	399	241
TBA 100-4	4	100	2900	width 230 height 240	240
TBA 100-6	6	100	3000	340	375
Bofors M70	6	135	3226	486	400

* without nose and tail fairings

Group 3a Bombs

Designation	Length (mm)	Diameter (mm)	Weight (kg)	Warhead (kg)	Explosive (kg)
Matra 250 kg (general purpose)	2120	320	250	–	
Matra 400 kg (general purpose)	2190	400	380	–	
Chinese Type 2 (blast bomb)	1500	450	473	–	200
Thomson-Brandt BAT120 (retarded + fragmentation)	1500	100	34	24	6
Thomson-Brandt BAP100 (runway-piercing)	1800	100	32.5	18	3.5
Matra Durandal (runway-piercing)	2491	223	219	100	15

Group 3b Bombs

The Spanish EXPAL BR series of low-drag, free-fall bombs is similar to the US Mk 80 series. The weights tabled below are evidently nominal values.

Designation	Length (mm)	Diameter (mm)	Weight (kg)	Explosive (kg)	US Equivalent
BR50	1380	180	50	23	
BR125	1820	240	125	57	Mk 81, 122 kg

BR250	2150	290	250	92	Mk 82, 241 kg
BR375	2805	330	375	171	
BR500	2940	360	500	206	Mk 83, 447 kg
BR1000	3820	460	1000	475	Mk 84, 893 kg

Group 3c Bombs

The corresponding retarded bombs are the BRP series, as below.

Designation	Length (mm)	Diameter (mm)	Weight (kg)	Explosive (kg)	US Equivalent
BRP50	1425	180	50	23	
BRP125	1820	240	125	57	Mk 81, 136 kg
BRP250	2123	290	250	92	Mk 82, 259 kg
BRP375	2855	330	375	171	
BRP500	2850	360	500	206	(no retd. Mk 83)

Group 3d Cluster Bomb Units

Designation	Length (cm)	CBU Dia (mm)	Weight (mm)	Bomblet (No)	Bomblet Weight (kg)	Explosive (kg)
Armscor CB470	2600	419	450	40	6.2	1.8
ISC Rockeye II	2400	335	222	247	0.61	0.18
Matra-TBA Beluga	3328	360	285	151	1.2	N/A
Hunting BL755	2438	419	273	147	1.1	0.225
Cardoen CB-130	2050	253	60	25	0.74	0.15
Cardoen CB-500	2640	446	254	50	0.74	0.15
Cardoen CB-1000	2265	497	454	80	0.74	0.15

Group 4a Tactical Air-Ground Guided Weapons

Designation	Length	Span (cm)	Weight (cm)	Warhead (kg)	Range (km)
Emerson AGM-123A Skipper II	433	160	582	(Mk 83)	25 +
Rockwell GBU-15	394	150	1187	(Mk 84)	9 +
Rockwell AGM-130A	394	150	1323	(Mk 84)	25 +
Hughes AGM-65E Maverick	249	72	293	136	20 +
Aérospatiale AS. 30L	365	100	520	240	10

Group 4b Anti-Tank Guided Weapons

Designation	Length (cm)	Span (cm)	Weight (kg)	Warhead (kg)	Range (km)
Hughes BGM-71D TOW-2	140	34	21.5	6.0	3.75
Euromissile HOT-2	127	31	23	6.5	4.0
Rockwell AGM-114A Hellfire	162.5	33	44.8	9.0	6.0

Group 4c Anti-Radar Guided Weapons

Designation	Length (cm)	Span (cm)	Weight (kg)	Warhead (kg)	Range (km)
TI AGM-45A Shrike	305	91.4	181	66	40
GD AGM-78D Standard	457	109	816	N/A	56
TI AGM-88A HARM	417	112	366	66	18.5
Matra ARMAT	412	120	550	150	100?

Group 4d Anti-Ship Guided Weapons

Designation	Length (cm)	Span (cm)	Weight (kg)	Warhead (kg)	Range (km)
Aérospatiale AS.15TT	230	56.4	103	30	15
BAe Sea Skua	250	72	145	20	15 +
Aérospatiale/MBB ANL	N/A	N/A	200	50	30
Hughes AGM-65F Maverick	249	72	307	136	20 +
Kongsberg Penguin Mk 2 Mod 7	296	140	340	121	27
Kongsberg Penguin Mk 3	320	100	350	121	40
Oto Melara Marte Mk 2	484	98	340	70	20 +
IAI Gabriel III	385	110	600	150	60
Aérospatiale AM. 39 Exocet	469	110	655	165	50-70
MBB Kormoran	440	100	630	160	30 +
MDC AGM-84 Harpoon	384	91.4	520	227	130 +
BAe Sea Eagle	414	120	600	230 +	110 +
SBMC RBS15F	435	140	600	N/A	70 +
IAI Gabriel IV	470	160	960	N/A	200
Aérospatiale/MBB ANS	570	N/A	950	180	180 +

Group 4e Medium/Long Range Guided Weapons

Designation	Length (cm)	Span (cm)	Weight (kg)	Warhead (kg)	Range (km)
MDC SLAM	450	91	628	220?	100 +
Aérospatiale ASMP	538	95.6	840	(300kT)	80-250
Boeing AGM-131A SRAM-2	427	N/A	816	nuclear	N/A
Boeing AGM-68B ALCM	632	366	1360	nuclear	2500

Group 5a Short-Range AAMs

Designation	Length (cm)	Span (cm)	Weight (kg)	Warhead (kg)	Range (km)
Ford/Raytheon AIM-9L/M	287	63.5	86.6	9.4	16 +
CATLIC PL-5B	289.2	65.7	85	N/A	16
Rafael Python 3	300	86	120	11	15
Matra Magic 2	274.8	66	90	N/A	N/A
Armscor Kukri	294	53	74.2	N/A	4
GD FIM-92A Stinger	152	9	14	3	5.5

Group 5b Medium/Long-Range AAMs

Designation	Length (cm)	Span (cm)	Weight (kg)	Warhead (kg)	Range (km)
Raytheon/GD AIM-7M	370	100	228	40	50
Selenia Aspide	370	100	220	35	N/A
BAe Sky Flash	366	102	193	30	40 +
Matra Super 530D	379.5	87.5	270	30 +	40 +
Matra MICA	310	N/A	110	N/A	50
Hughes/Raytheon AIM-120	360	62.7	148	22.7	70?
Hughes AIM-54C Phoenix	395	91	458	60	200

Abbreviations

AAA	anti-aircraft artillery
AAAM	Advanced Air-Air Missile
AAM	air-air missile
AASM	Advanced Air-Surface Missile (now SRAM-2)
AATCP	*Air-Air Très Courte Portée*
ABA	*Anti-Blindage Actif*
ABL	*Anti-Blindé Léger*
ACE	*Avion de Combat Européen*
ACM	Advanced Cruise Missile
AFB	Air Force Base
AFSA	*Affût Sabord* (door-mounted pintle) (FN)
AIR	Air-Inflatable Retarder
AIWS	Advanced Interdiction Weapons System
ALARM	Air-Launched Anti-Radar Missile
ALCM	Air-Launched Cruise Missile
ALMV	Air-Launched Miniature Vehicle
AMRAAM	Advanced Medium-Range Air-Air Missile
AMV	*Anti-Matériel et Véhicule*
ANL	*Anti-Navire Léger*
ANS	*Anti-Navire Supersonique*
AOA	angle of attack
APDS	armour-piercing, discarding-sabot
API	armour-piercing, incendiary
ARDC	Armament Research and Development Center

ARDU	Aircraft Research & Development Unit
ARM	anti-radar missile
ARMAT	Anti-Radar MATra
ASAT	Anti-SATellite
ASM	air-surface missile
ASMP	*Air-Sol Moyenne Portée*
ASRAAM	Advanced Short-Range Air-Air Missile
AST	Air Staff Target
ASW	*Anti-Shelter Wirkkoerper* (RTG)
ATA	Advanced Tactical Aircraft
ATAS	Air-To-Air Stinger
ATB	Advanced Technology Bomber
ATF	Advanced Tactical Fighter
ATGW	anti-tank guided weapon
BAe	British Aerospace
BALLUTE	BALLoon-parachUTE
BGL	*Bombe Guidée par Laser* (Matra)
BKEP	Bomb, Kinetic Energy Penetrator
BVR	beyond visual range
CASA	*Construcciones Aeronauticas SA*
CASMU	*Consorzio Armamenti Spendibili Multi-Uso*
CATH	Common-Anti-Tank Helicopter
CATIC	China National Aero-Technology Export/Import Corp
CBU	cluster bomb unit
CEAM	*Centre d'Experimentation Aérienne Militaire*
CEM	Combined Effects Munition
CEM	*Combiné d'Emport Multiple* (Dassault-Breguet)
CEP	circle of equal probability
CEV	*Centre d'Essais en Vol*
CHAG	Compact High-performance Aerial Gun
CIWS	close-in weapon system
c/n	construction number
CRV	Canadian Rocket Vehicle
CWS	Container Weapon System (MBB)
CWW	Cruciform-Wing Weapon
DAACM	Direct Airfield Attack Combined Munition
DEM	*démolition* (Thomson-Brandt)
Do	*Dornier*
DU	depleted uranium
DWS	Dispenser Weapon System
ECM	electronic countermeasures
EFA	European Fighter Aircraft
EMDG	EuroMissile Dynamics Group
EOCM	electro-optical countermeasures
ERAM	Extended-Range Anti-armor Munition

FAC	forward air control (ler)
FAE	fuel-air explosives
FASCAM	FAmily of SCAtterable Mines
FFAR	Folding-Fin Aircraft Rocket
FFV	*Forenade FabriksVerken*
FN	*Fabrique Nationale Herstal SA*
FPB	fast patrol boat
FY	fiscal year
FZ	*Les Forges de Zeebrugge*
GBU	glide bomb unit
GE	General Electric
GIAT	*Groupement Industriel des Armaments Terrestres*
GP	general purpose
GPS	Global Positioning System
GW	guided weapon
HAAC	helicopter air-air combat
HAC	*Hélicoptère Anti-Char*
HAP	*Hélicoptère d'Appui et de Protection*
HARM	High-speed Anti-Radar Missile
HEI	high explosive, incendiary
HELLFIRE	HELicopter-Launched FIRE-and forget (Rockwell)
HMP	heavy machine gun pod (FN)
HTM	Hard Target Munition
HUD-WAC	head-up display and weapon-aiming computer
HVAR	High-Velocity Aircraft Rocket
HVM	Hyper-Velocity Missile
IAI	Israel Aircraft Industries
IIR	imaging infra-red
IOC	initial operational capability
IR	infra-red
ISC	International Signal and Control
KB	*Kleine Bombe* (RTG)
KG	*KampfGeschwader*
LAD	Low Altitude Dispenser (Brunswick Corp)
LAMPS	Light Airborne Multi-Purpose System
LDGP	low drag, general purpose
LGB	laser-guided bomb
LLFS	linear linkless feed system (GE)
LOCPOD	LOw-Cost Powered Off-boresight Dispenser
MALS	Miniature Air-Launched System
MARTEL	*Missile Anti-Radar et TELevision* (BAe/Matra)
MBB	*Messerschmitt-Boelkow-Blohm*
MCAS	Marine Corps Air Station
MDS	Modular Dispenser System
Me	*Messerschmitt*

MHV	Miniature Homing Vehicle
MICA	*Missile d'Interception et de Combat*
MoBiDiC	Modular Bird with Dispenser-Container
MoU	memorandum of understanding
MRBF	mean rounds between failures
MRL	modular rocket launcher (FN)
MSOW	Modular Stand-Off Weapon
MTG	main target group
MW	*MehrZweckwaffe*
NAS	Naval Air Station
NATO	North Atlantic Treaty Organisation
NORINCO	North China Industries Corp
OCU	Operational Conversion Unit (RAF)
PAH	*PanzerAbwehrHubschrauber*
PCAP	pitch-compensated armament pylon (Sikorsky)
PIP	product improvement program
R&D	research and development
RAF	Royal Air Force
RF	radio frequency
RFC	Royal Flying Corps
RN	Royal Navy
RNAS	Royal Naval Air Station
RNoAF	Royal Norwegian Air Force
RP	rocket projectile
RTG	*Raketen Technik GmbH*
SAC	Strategic Air Command (USAF)
SACLOS	semi-active command to line-of-sight
SAM	surface-air missile
SAPHEI	semi-armour-piercing, high explosive incendiary
SBMC	Saab-Bofors Missile Corp
SEAD	suppression of enemy air defences
SEAM	Sidewinder Extended Acquisition Mode
SFA	*Système de Freinage et d'Amorcage*
SFW	Sensor-Fuzed Weapon (Avco)
SLAM	Stand-off Land-Attack Missile
SMABL	*sous-munition anti-blindé*
SMAP	*sous-munition anti-piste*
SRAM	Short-Range Attack Missile
SRARM	Short-Range Anti-Radar Missile
STABO	*STArtbahnBOmbe* (RTG)
STAR	*Supersonique Tactique Anti-Radar* (Matra)
SUAWACS	Soviet Union Airborne Warning and Control System
TBA	*Thomson-Brandt Armaments*
TER	triple ejection rack
TFW	tactical fighter wing

TI	Texas Instruments
TMD	Tactical Munitions Dispenser (Marquardt)
TOW	Tube-launched Optically-tracked Wire-guided (Hughes)
UHF	ultra-high frequency
USAAF	United States Army Air Force
USAF	United States Air Force
USMC	United States Marine Corps
USN	United States Navy
VBW	Vertical Ballistic Weapon (MBB)
VHF	very high frequency
WAM	Wide Area Mine (Avco)
WW	World War